11+
Non-verbal Reasoning
Non-verbal Reasoning Technique

WORKBOOK 2

Dr Stephen C Curran
with Andrea Richardson

Edited by Katrina MacKay

This book belongs to

Accelerated Education Publications Ltd.

Contents

Chapter Six
COMPONENTS

The **Components** of Non-verbal Reasoning comprise:
Key Questions • **Elimination Skills** • **Descriptive Skills**

1. Key Questions in NVR

All NVR questions are centred around three key areas:
1) The shape most **Similar** 2) The shape most **Different**
3) The next shape in a **Series** of shapes (identify a pattern).

2. Elimination Skills

Eliminating the wrong options one by one, by marking them or crossing them out, helps to identify the answer.

Example: | Which shape is most like the Test Shape? |

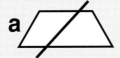 a  b c d

Test Shape

Answer: **d** - It is four-sided and has a Grey Fill.

3. Descriptive Skills

Descriptive Skills in Non-verbal Reasoning aid understanding.
A summary of descriptive skills is given below:
Elements • Movements • Manipulations • Patterns • Layering

a. Elements
(i) Shapes

Standard Shapes comprise all 'closed' geometrically defined shapes. **Rectangle**   **Specialist Shapes** comprise everyday recognisable 'closed' shapes. **Boat**

(ii) Fills

'Closed' shape **Fills** comprise five different categories:

Block	**Shaded**	**Cross-hatched**	**Liquid**	**Dotted**
Black Grey White	Horizontal Vertical Slanted	Squares Lattice	Speckled (Dark) Mottled (Light)	Close Spaced

(iii) Lines

All **Line Types** have three main properties:	1. Solid Dashed Dotted 2. Straight Curved 3. Thin Thick	**Line Shapes** comprise recognisable 'open' shapes. **Wave** The line type is: **Solid, Curved, Thin**

b. Movements

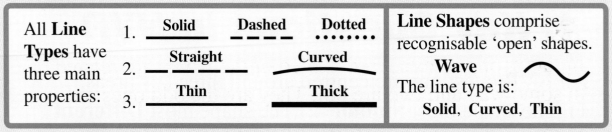

In Non-verbal Reasoning, shapes can **Move** in four different ways:

Reflect — Line of Symmetry

Rotate — Clockwise or Anticlockwise 45° 90° 180°

Superimpose — Merger; Linkage; Overlay; Enclosure

Transpose — Vertical or Horizontal

c. Manipulations

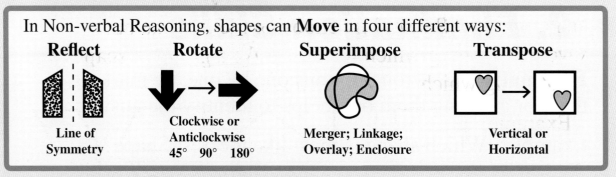

In Non-verbal Reasoning, shapes can be **Manipulated** in the following four ways:

Size — Enlarge/Reduce

Addition — Shapes and parts of shapes

Subtraction — Shapes and parts of shapes

Frequency — Counting

d. Patterns

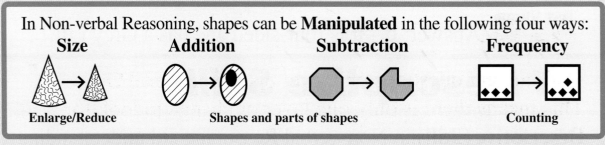

In Non-verbal Reasoning, shapes can make **Patterns** in two different ways:

Repetition

Cumulation

e. Layering

Layering occurs when changes to shapes or figures are combined. Questions with up to five layers or changes can seem complex. **This book involves learning to identify & describe these layers.**

Chapter Seven
ODD ONE OUT

In Verbal Reasoning, choosing the **Odd One Out** involves seeing how the meaning of each word in a group of words relates to the other words.

Example:

In this group of five words, three of the words are related in some way and two are not. They are the odd ones out.

ash   branch   oak   leaf   willow

branch and **leaf** are odd ones out as they are not tree types.

In Non-verbal Reasoning, choosing the odd one out involves spotting which likeness links a group of shapes and identifying which shape does not have this likeness.

Example:

All the shapes have four sides except the Triangle which only has three sides, so this is the odd one out.

1. Basic Level

Odd one out questions only ever operate at Level One. This means there is only one layer or change to look for. On easier questions we can spot this very quickly.

Example: | Which shape is most unlike the others?

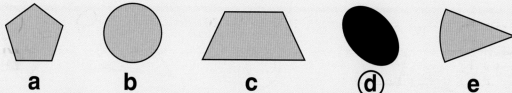

a   b   c   ⓓ   e

Answer: **d**

All the shapes have a Grey Fill except the Ellipse, which has a Black Fill, making it the odd one out.

Exercise 7: 1   Which shape or figure is the odd one out?

1)   **a**   **b**   **c**   **d**   **e**

Why? It is the only shape that does not have a

Block Fill.   Answer e ✓

2)   **a**   **b**   **c**   **d**   **e**

Why? because it is the only one with

4 sides   Answer d ✓

3)   **a**   **b**   **c**   **d**   **e**

Why? _____

_____ Answer e ✓

4)   **a**   **b**   **c**   **d**   **e**

Why? _____

_____ Answer e ✓

5)   **a**   **b**   **c**   **d**   **e**

Why? _____

_____ Answer d

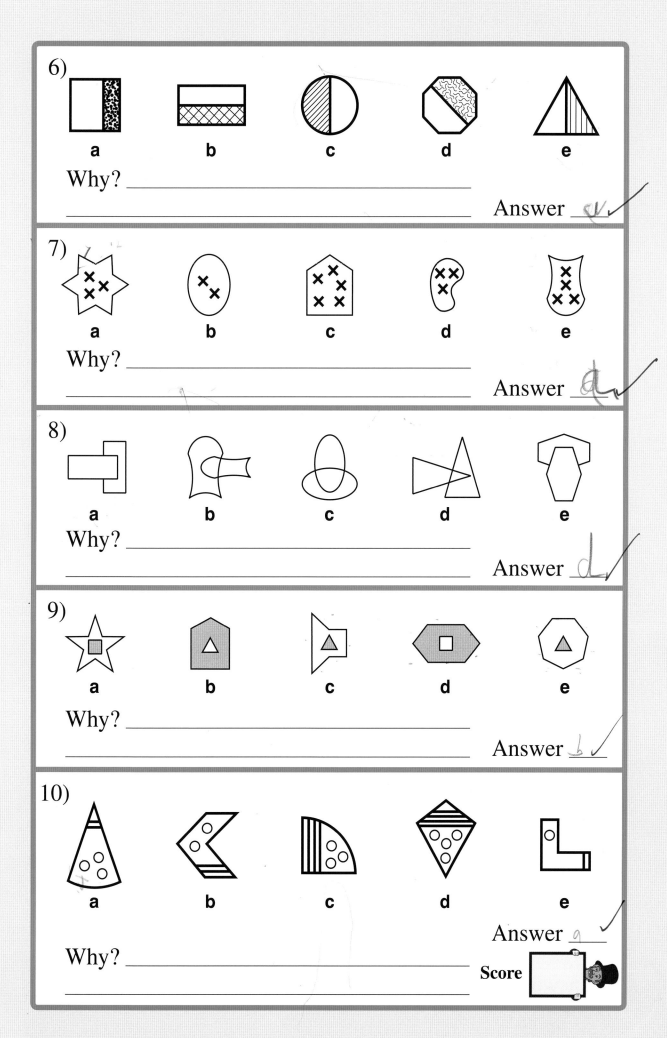

6)

a   b   c   d   e

Why? _____

_____ Answer __e__

7)

a   b   c   d   e

Why? _____

_____ Answer __d__

8)

a   b   c   d   e

Why? _____

_____ Answer __d__

9)

a   b   c   d   e

Why? _____

_____ Answer __b__

10)

a   b   c   d   e

Answer __a__

Why? _____

_____ **Score**

Chapter Eight
CODES

The skill of **Decoding** in Verbal Reasoning involves finding out what the letters or numbers represent.

For example: If **678** means **PIT**, what does **876** mean?

Each digit represents a letter. Answer: **TIP**

In Non-verbal Reasoning, letters are often used to represent:

Shapes • **Fills** • **Lines**

1. Type 1 - Level Two

Decoding in Non-verbal Reasoning involves working out which letters go with which shapes. A **Level Two** code question has two letters which represent the correct shape. Level One (one letter) questions are too easy for tests.

Example: Which pair of letters represents the Test Shape?

MA

MB   Test Shape   NB   MB   MC   AM   NA
                         a   b   c   d   e

NC

The Code Rules are as follows:

Layer One - **M** stands for Squares; **N** stands for Triangles.
Layer Two - **A** stands for a White Fill; **B** for a Grey Fill; **C** for a Black Fill.

NB   MB   MC   AM   NA
 a   b   c   d   e

It is important to **eliminate** the wrong possibilities:

a and **e** - **NB** and **NA** are incorrect because they stand for Triangles.
b - **MB** is incorrect because **B** stands for a Grey Fill.
d - **AM** is incorrect because **A** stands for a White Fill and the letters are not in the correct order, which is not permitted.

Answer: **c** - **M** stands for Square; **C** stands for a Black Fill.

Exercise 8: 1

Which pair of letters on the right represents the Test Shape or Figure?

1)

ES

FS

ET

Test Shape

FS	ET	FT	ES	TF
a	b	c	d	e

Code Rules:

i) _E - Sector Shape; F - Cross Shape._

ii) _S - Grey Fill; T - Black Fill._

Answer __c__

2)

PJ

PK

QJ

Test Figure

JQ	PJ	JP	QK	QJ
a	b	c	d	e

Code Rules:

i) _____

ii) _____

Answer __d__

3)

AR

BS

AT

Test Shape

BR	TA	SB	BT	AS
a	b	c	d	e

Code Rules:

i) _____

ii) _____

Answer __d__

4)

VG

WH

XG

Test Shape

WG	VX	XH	GX	VH
a	b	c	d	e

Code Rules:

i) _____

ii) _____

Answer __e__

5)

CO

DP

CP

Test Shape

OP	DO	OD	PO	DC
a	b	c	d	e

Code Rules:

i) _____

ii) _____

Answer __d__

ae © 2015 Stephen Curran

6)

☆ ZM

⬟ YN

《 XM

★ **Test Figure**

YM	ZN	XN	MZ	ZY
a	**b**	**c**	**d**	**e**

Code Rules:

i) _____

ii) _____

Answer _b_ ✓

---

7)

UF

⇨ VG

UH

Test Shape

VF	GU	VH	VG	UG
a	**b**	**c**	**d**	**e**

Code Rules:

i) _____

ii) _____

Answer _C_ ✓

---

8)

◑ JR

◐ KS

⊖ JT

● LR

● **Test Figure**

LT	LS	JT	KT	JS
a	**b**	**c**	**d**	**e**

Code Rules:

i) _____

ii) _____

Answer _a_ ✓

---

9)

△⊕ SD

▢✚ TE

✦✚ TF

✦⊕ **Test Figure**

SD	SE	DS	TD	SF
a	**b**	**c**	**d**	**e**

Code Rules:

i) _____

ii) _____

Answer _e_ ✓

---

10)

AL

BM

CN

AM

Test Figure

CM	BL	AN	CL	BN
a	**b**	**c**	**d**	**e**

Code Rules:

i) _____

ii) _____

Answer

Score

2. Type 2 - Level Two

Type 2 code questions look different but work in the same way as Type 1. This type only ever has two letters, so it always functions as a Level Two question.

Example: | Which two letters represent the Test Figure?

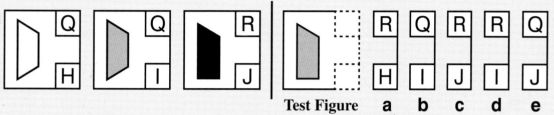

Test Figure   a   b   c   d   e

The Code Rules are as follows:

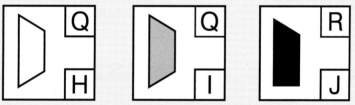

Layer One - Q stands for an Isosceles Trapezium;
R stands for an ordinary Trapezium.
Layer Two - H stands for a White Fill; **I** for a Grey Fill; **J** for a Black Fill.

The Set of Codes:

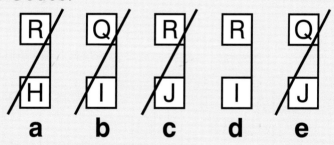

a   b   c   d   e

It is important to **eliminate** the wrong possibilities:
b and **e** - **QI** and **QJ** are incorrect because they stand for the wrong shape.
a - **RH** is incorrect because **H** stands for a White Fill.
c - **RJ** is incorrect because **J** stands for a Black Fill.

The Test Shape and the Correct Code:

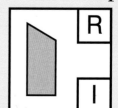

Layer One
R stands for an ordinary Trapezium.
Layer Two
I stands for a Grey Fill.

Answer: **d** - **RI** is the correct code.

Exercise 8: 2

Which pair of letters on the right represents the Test Figure?

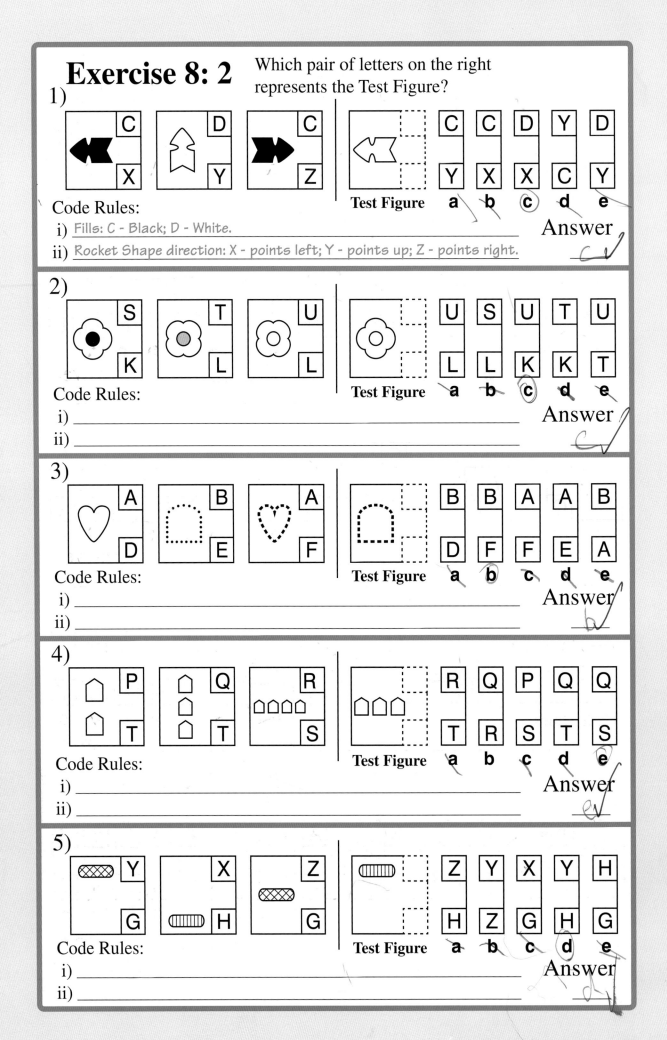

1)

Code Rules:
i) Fills: C - Black; D - White.
ii) Rocket Shape direction: X - points left; Y - points up; Z - points right.

Test Figure   a   b   c   d   e

Answer

2)

Code Rules:
i) _____
ii) _____

Test Figure   a   b   c   d   e

Answer

3)

Code Rules:
i) _____
ii) _____

Test Figure   a   b   c   d   e

Answer

4)

Code Rules:
i) _____
ii) _____

Test Figure   a   b   c   d   e

Answer

5)

Code Rules:
i) _____
ii) _____

Test Figure   a   b   c   d   e

Answer

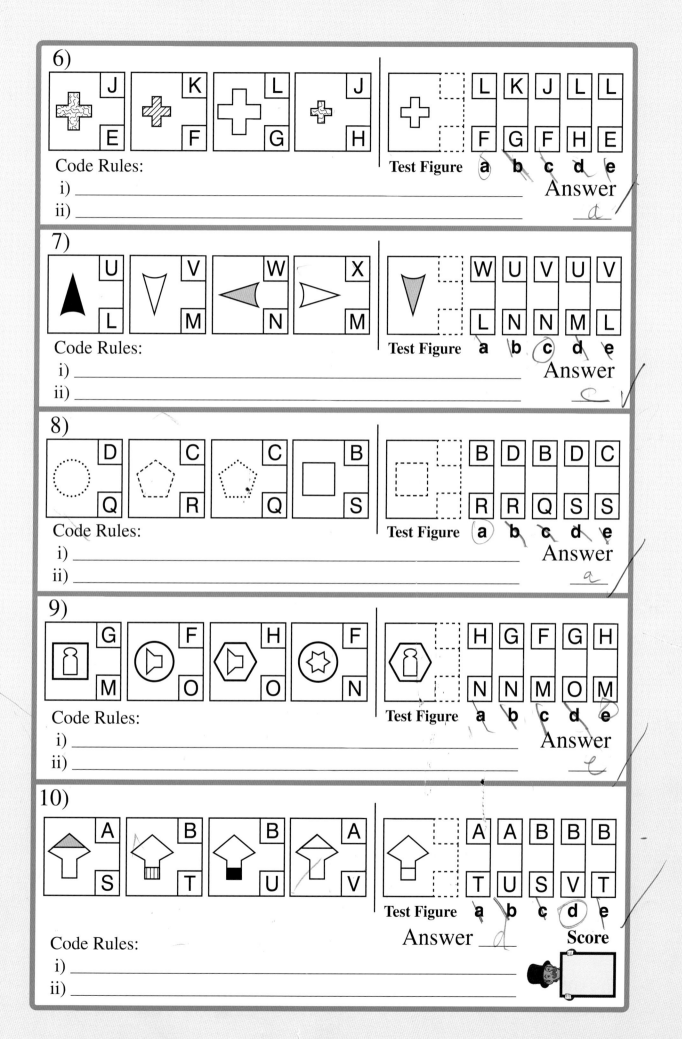

6)

J E | K F | L G | J H | Test Figure

L F	K G	J F	L H	L E
a	**b**	**c**	**d**	**e**

Code Rules:
  i) _____
  ii) _____

Answer _____ *a*

7)

U L | V M | W N | X M | Test Figure

W L	U N	V N	U M	V L
a	**b**	**c**	**d**	**e**

Code Rules:
  i) _____
  ii) _____

Answer _____ *c*

8)

D Q | C R | C Q | B S | Test Figure

B R	D R	B Q	D S	C S
a	**b**	**c**	**d**	**e**

Code Rules:
  i) _____
  ii) _____

Answer _____ *a*

9)

G M | F O | H O | F N | Test Figure

H N	G N	F M	G O	H M
a	**b**	**c**	**d**	**e**

Code Rules:
  i) _____
  ii) _____

Answer _____ *e*

10)

A S | B T | B U | A V | Test Figure

A T	A U	B S	B V	B T
a	**b**	**c**	**d**	**e**

Answer _____ *d*   **Score**

Code Rules:
  i) _____
  ii) _____

3. Type 1 - Level Three

A **Level Three** code question has three letters which represent the correct shape.

Example: | Which three letters represent the Test Figure? |

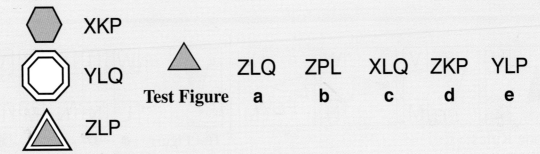

Test Figure	ZLQ	ZPL	XLQ	ZKP	YLP
	a	b	c	d	e

The Code Rules are as follows:

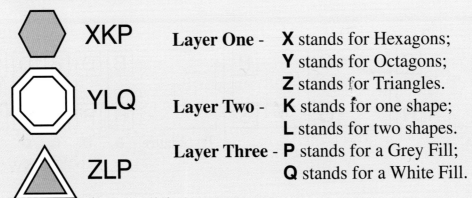

Layer One - **X** stands for Hexagons;
Y stands for Octagons;
Z stands for Triangles.

Layer Two - **K** stands for one shape;
L stands for two shapes.

Layer Three - **P** stands for a Grey Fill;
Q stands for a White Fill.

The Set of Codes:

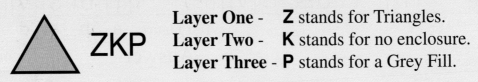

Z̶L̶Q	Z̶P̶L	X̶L̶Q	ZKP	Y̶L̶P̶
a	b	c	d	e

It is important to **eliminate** the wrong possibilities:

c and **e** - **XLQ** and **YLP** are incorrect as they stand for the wrong shapes.

a - **ZLQ** is incorrect because **L** stands for enclosed shapes and **Q** stands for shapes with a White Fill.

b - **ZPL** is incorrect because **L** stands for enclosed shapes. The letters are also in the wrong order which is not permitted.

The Test Shape and the Correct Code:

ZKP **Layer One** - **Z** stands for Triangles.
Layer Two - **K** stands for no enclosure.
Layer Three - **P** stands for a Grey Fill.

Answer: **d** - **ZKP** is the correct code.

Exercise 8: 3

Which three letters on the right represent the Test Figure?

1)

SXA

TYA

SZB

Test Figure

TXA   TYB   SXB   TXB   TZB
a   b   c   d   e

Answer ____

Code Rules:
i) S - Hexagon horizontal; T - Hexagon vertical.
ii) X - Black Fill; Y - White Fill; Z - Grey Fill.
iii) A, B - direction of Sector Shapes.

2)

FBV

GAV

GBW

Test Figure

FBW   GAW   FAV   FAW   GBV
a   b   c   d   e

Answer __d__

Code Rules:
i) ____
ii) ____
iii) ____

3)

LRD

MSE

LTE

Test Figure

MTE   MRD   LSD   LTD   MTD
a   b   c   d   e

Answer __c__

Code Rules:
i) ____
ii) ____
iii) ____

4)

PGC

QGB

QHC

Test Figure

PHC   PGB   PHB   QHB   QGC
a   b   c   d   e

Answer __b__

Code Rules:
i) ____
ii) ____
iii) ____

5)

JXT

JYU

KZT

Test Figure

JXU   KXU   KYU   KZU   KXT
a   b   c   d   e

Answer __b__

Code Rules:
i) ____
ii) ____
iii) ____

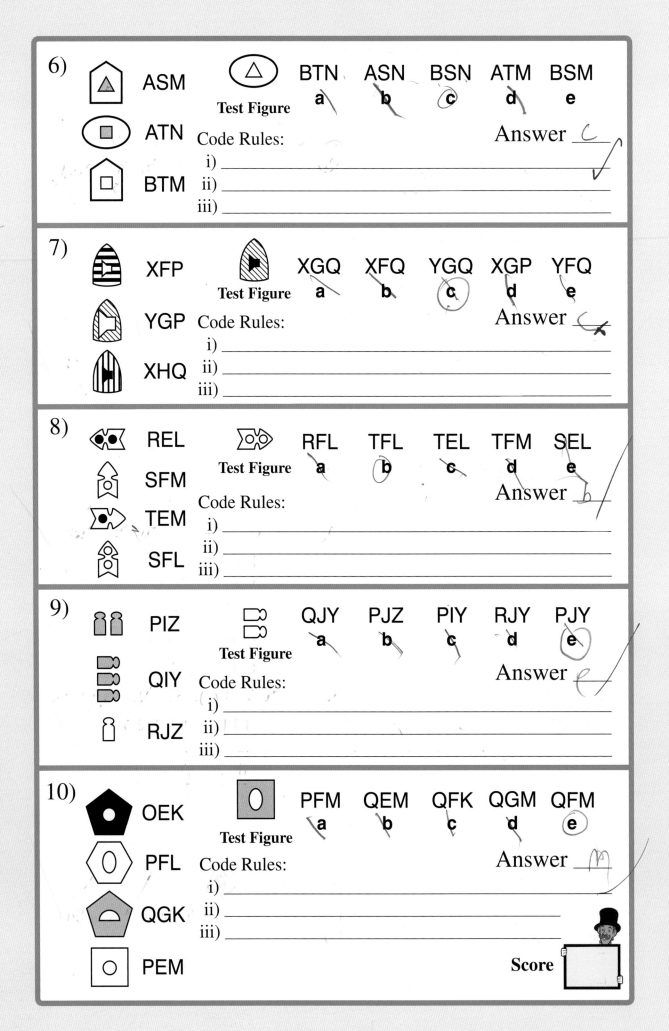

6) ASM ATN BTM

Test Figure

BTN **a** ASN **b** BSN **c** ATM **d** BSM **e**

Answer _c_

Code Rules:
i) _____
ii) _____
iii) _____

7) XFP YGP XHQ

Test Figure

XGQ **a** XFQ **b** YGQ **c** XGP **d** YFQ **e**

Answer _c_

Code Rules:
i) _____
ii) _____
iii) _____

8) REL SFM TEM SFL

Test Figure

RFL **a** TFL **b** TEL **c** TFM **d** SEL **e**

Answer _b_

Code Rules:
i) _____
ii) _____
iii) _____

9) PIZ QIY RJZ

Test Figure

QJY **a** PJZ **b** PIY **c** RJY **d** PJY **e**

Answer _e_

Code Rules:
i) _____
ii) _____
iii) _____

10) OEK PFL QGK PEM

Test Figure

PFM **a** QEM **b** QFK **c** QGM **d** QFM **e**

Answer _e_

Code Rules:
i) _____
ii) _____
iii) _____

Score

Chapter Nine
ANALOGIES

In Verbal Reasoning, an **Analogy** is a similarity in meaning between two parallel statements or words. This comparison is linked by the word '**as**' which means '**like**'.

For example: **Huge** is to **tiny** as **wide** is to **narrow**

In a Non-verbal Reasoning analogy question, a similarity can be established between two sets of shapes.

Example:

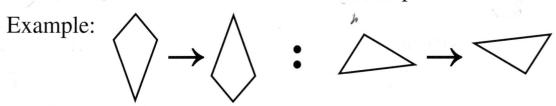

The first Kite Shape has been rotated 180° to form the second Kite Shape. The **Colon Symbol** (**:**) in between means '**as**' or '**like**'. Therefore the first Triangle must be rotated 180° to form the second Triangle. This now completes the analogy between the two sets of shapes.

1. Level One

In a **Level One** analogy question, there is only one layer or change to look for within the first pair of shapes. This layer or change will then be applied to the second pair of shapes.

Example: | Which shape completes the analogy? |

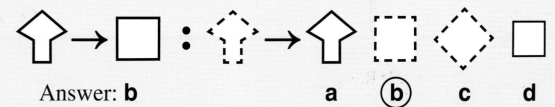

Answer: **b**   a   (b)   c   d

The Analogy Rule: In the first pair of shapes the Arrow Shape with a Solid Line becomes a Square with a Solid Line.
The Analogy Rule Applied: In the second pair of shapes the Arrow Shape with a Dashed Line becomes a Square with a Dashed Line.

Exercise 9: 1
Which shape or figure completes the analogy?

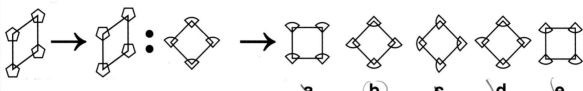

a **b** **c** **d** **e**

1) Analogy Rule: Answer

The Linked shapes rotate 180° or reflect.   b ✓

a **b** **c** **d** **e**

2) Analogy Rule: Answer

_____   d ✓

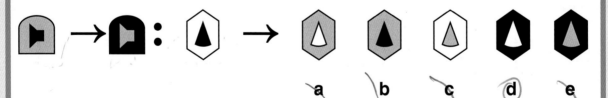

a **b** **c** **d** **e**

3) Analogy Rule: Answer

_____   e ✓

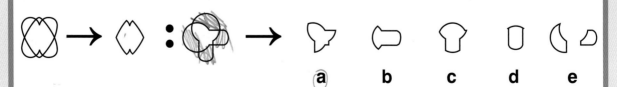

a **b** **c** **d** **e**

4) Analogy Rule: Answer

_____   d ✓

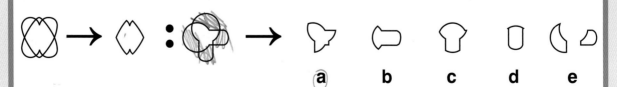

a **b** **c** **d** **e**

5) Analogy Rule: Answer

_____   a ✓

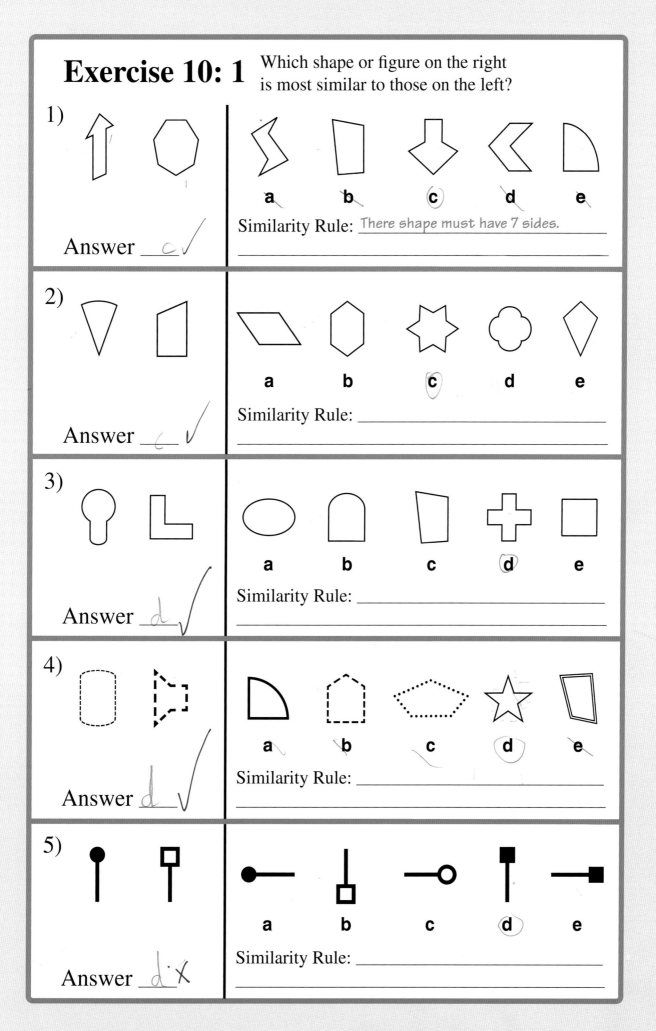

Exercise 10: 1

Which shape or figure on the right is most similar to those on the left?

1)

a   b   ⓒ   d   e

Similarity Rule: There shape must have 7 sides.

Answer __c__ ✓

2)

a   b   ⓒ   d   e

Similarity Rule: _____

Answer __c__ ✓

3)

a   b   c   ⓓ   e

Similarity Rule: _____

Answer __d__ ✓

4)

a   b   c   ⓓ   e

Similarity Rule: _____

Answer __d__ ✓

5)

a   b   c   ⓓ   e

Similarity Rule: _____

Answer __d__ ✗

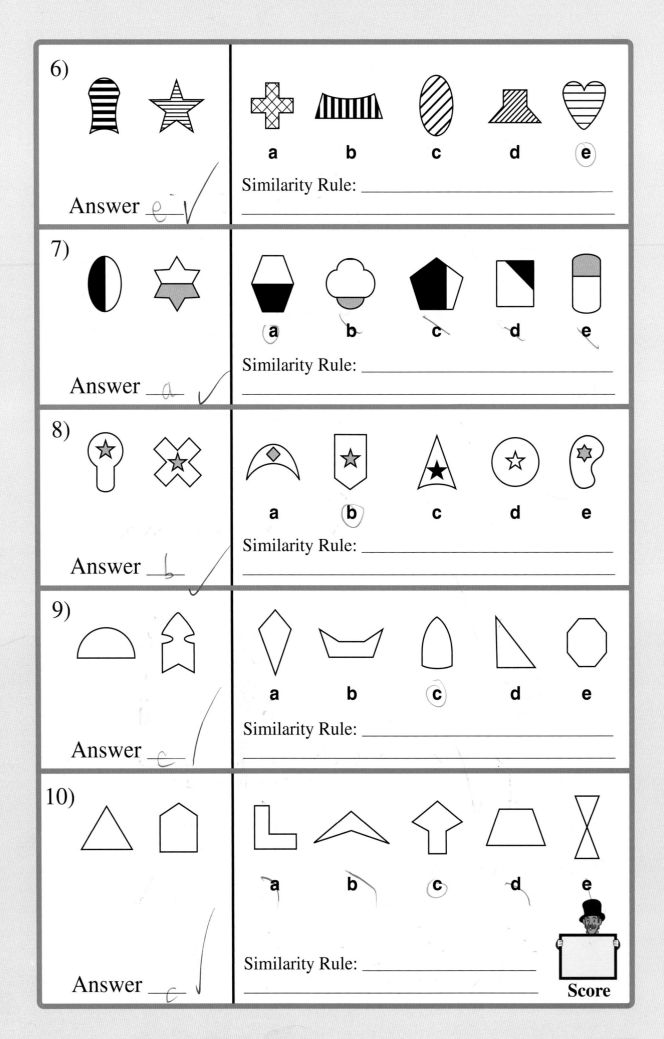

6)

Answer _e_ ✓

Similarity Rule: _____
_____

a   b   c   d   (e)

7)

Answer _a_ ✓

Similarity Rule: _____
_____

(a)   b   c   d   e

8)

Answer _b_ ✓

Similarity Rule: _____
_____

a   (b)   c   d   e

9)

Answer _c_ ✓

Similarity Rule: _____
_____

a   b   (c)   d   e

10)

Answer _c_ ✓

Similarity Rule: _____
_____

a   b   c   d   e

Score

2. Level Two

In **Level Two** similarity questions, there are two layers or similarities to look for between the figures.

Example: | Which figure on the right is most like the two figures on the left?

    a   b   c   d

The Rules of Similarity:

Layer 1 - The shapes must be identical or completely different.
Layer 2 - The shapes must be in groups of two or three.

Remember: The rules are only relevant if they help to select the right alternative and eliminate the wrong ones.

The Set of Figures:

    a   b   c   d

It is important to **eliminate** the wrong possibilities:
a - There are two identical shapes and one shape is different.
b - There should only be two or three shapes.
c - There are two identical shapes and one shape is different.

The Correct Figure:

This figure follows the rules of similarity.
Layer 1 - All the Triangles are identical.
Layer 2 - The Triangles are in a group of three.

Answer: **d**

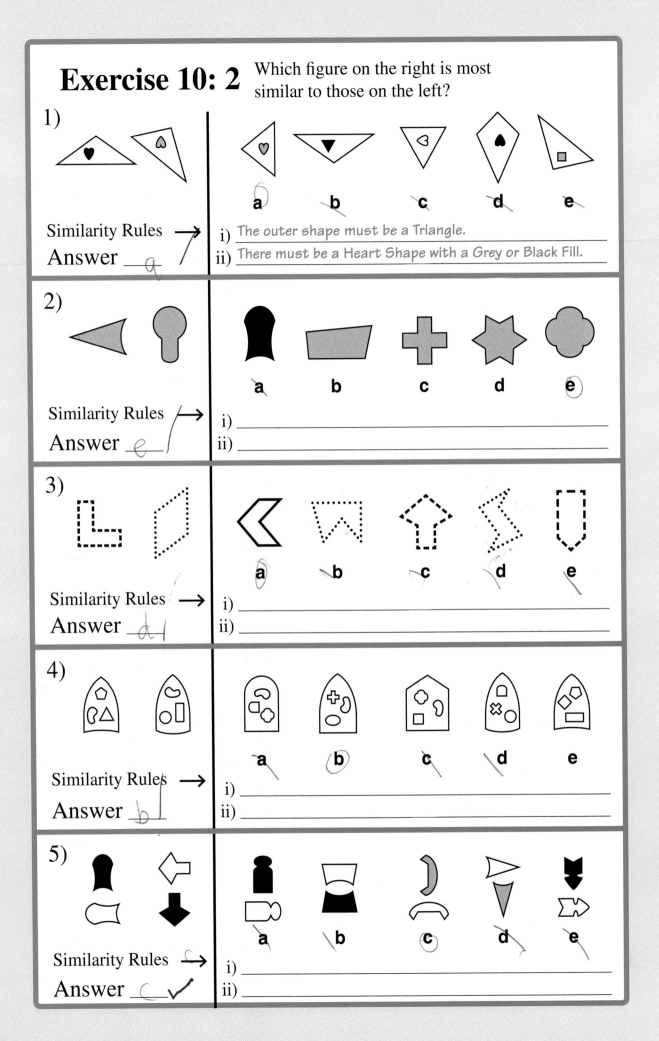

Exercise 10: 2

Which figure on the right is most similar to those on the left?

1)

Similarity Rules →
Answer _____ a

i) The outer shape must be a Triangle.
ii) There must be a Heart Shape with a Grey or Black Fill.

2)

Similarity Rules →
Answer _____ e

i) _____
ii) _____

3)

Similarity Rules →
Answer _____ a

i) _____
ii) _____

4)

Similarity Rules →
Answer _____ b

i) _____
ii) _____

5)

Similarity Rules →
Answer _____ c

i) _____
ii) _____

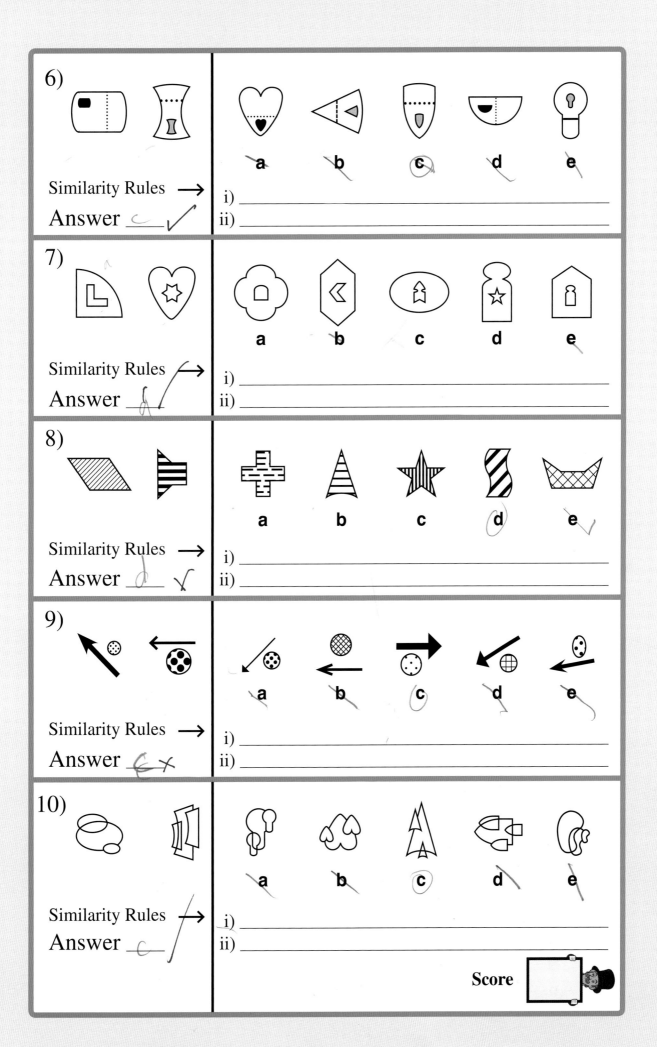

6)

Similarity Rules →

Answer _c_ ✓

i) _____

ii) _____

7)

Similarity Rules →

Answer _d_

i) _____

ii) _____

8)

Similarity Rules →

Answer _d_ ✓

i) _____

ii) _____

9)

Similarity Rules →

Answer _e✗_

i) _____

ii) _____

10)

Similarity Rules →

Answer _c_ ✓

i) _____

ii) _____

Score

3. Level Three

In **Level Three** similarity questions, there are three layers or similarities to look for between the figures.

Example: | Which figure on the right is most like the two figures on the left?

The Rules of Similarity:

Layer 1 - The Arrow Shapes are the same size.
Layer 2 - The Arrow Shape with a Grey Fill always overlays the second Arrow Shape.
Layer 3 - The two Arrow Shapes are related by rotation (a rotational difference of 90°).

Remember: The rules are only relevant if they help to select the right alternative and eliminate the wrong ones.

The Set of Figures:

It is important to **eliminate** the wrong possibilities:

a - The Arrow Shapes are not rotations but inversions of each other.
b - The Arrow Shape with a White Fill forms the overlay.
d - The Arrow Shape with a White Fill is smaller than the other Arrow Shape.

The Correct Figure:

This figure follows the rules of similarity.

Layer 1 - Both Arrow Shapes are the same size.
Layer 2 - The Arrow Shape with a Grey Fill overlays the second Arrow Shape with a Black Fill.
Layer 3 - The two Arrow Shapes are related by rotation (a rotational difference of 90°).

Answer: **c**

Exercise 10: 3

Which figure on the right is most similar to those on the left?

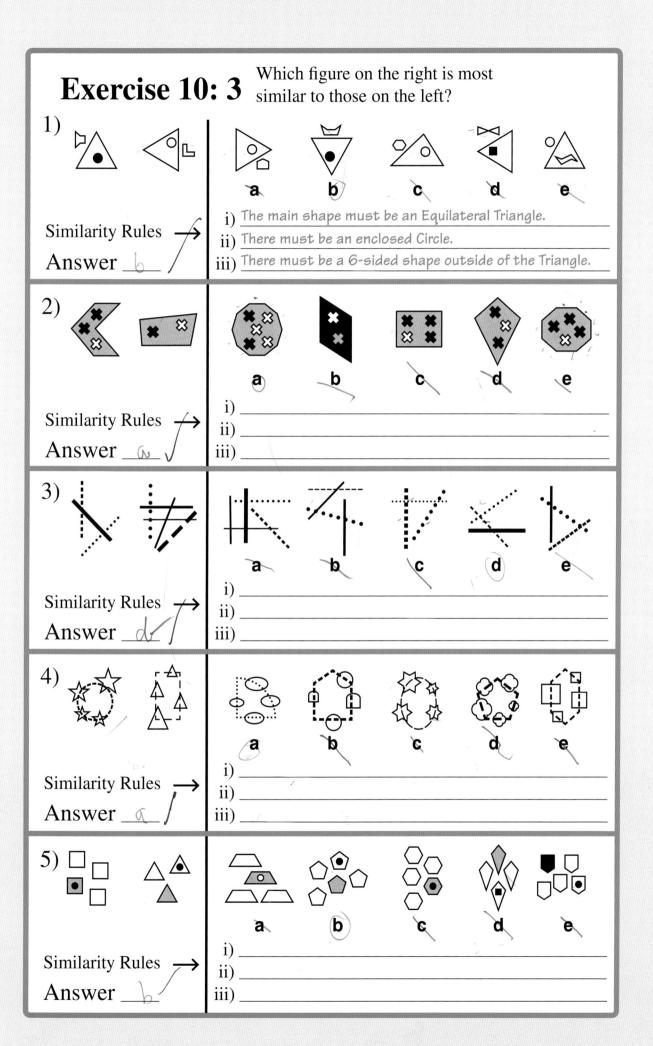

1)

a   b   c   d   e

Similarity Rules →

Answer _b_

i) The main shape must be an Equilateral Triangle.
ii) There must be an enclosed Circle.
iii) There must be a 6-sided shape outside of the Triangle.

2)

a   b   c   d   e

Similarity Rules →

Answer _a_

i) _____
ii) _____
iii) _____

3)

a   b   c   d   e

Similarity Rules →

Answer _d_

i) _____
ii) _____
iii) _____

4)

a   b   c   d   e

Similarity Rules →

Answer _a_

i) _____
ii) _____
iii) _____

5)

a   b   c   d   e

Similarity Rules →

Answer _b_

i) _____
ii) _____
iii) _____

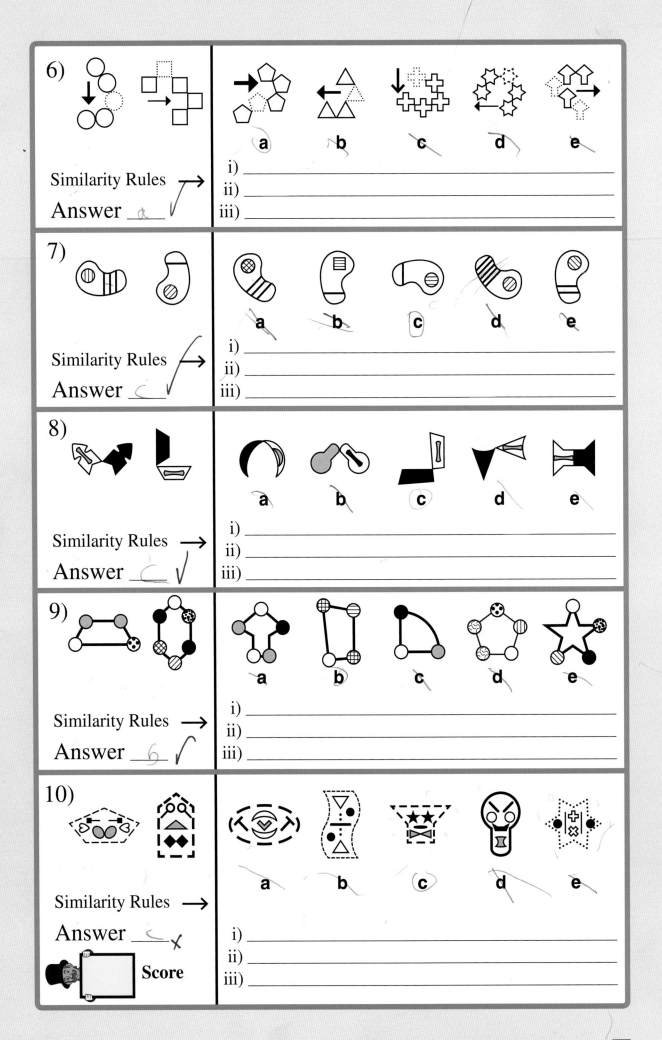

6)

Similarity Rules →

Answer _a_ ✓

i) _____
ii) _____
iii) _____

7)

Similarity Rules →

Answer _c_ ✓

i) _____
ii) _____
iii) _____

8)

Similarity Rules →

Answer _c_ ✓

i) _____
ii) _____
iii) _____

9)

Similarity Rules →

Answer _b_ ✓

i) _____
ii) _____
iii) _____

10)

Similarity Rules →

Answer _c_ ✗

Score

i) _____
ii) _____
iii) _____

Exercise 10: 1

Which shape or figure on the right is most similar to those on the left?

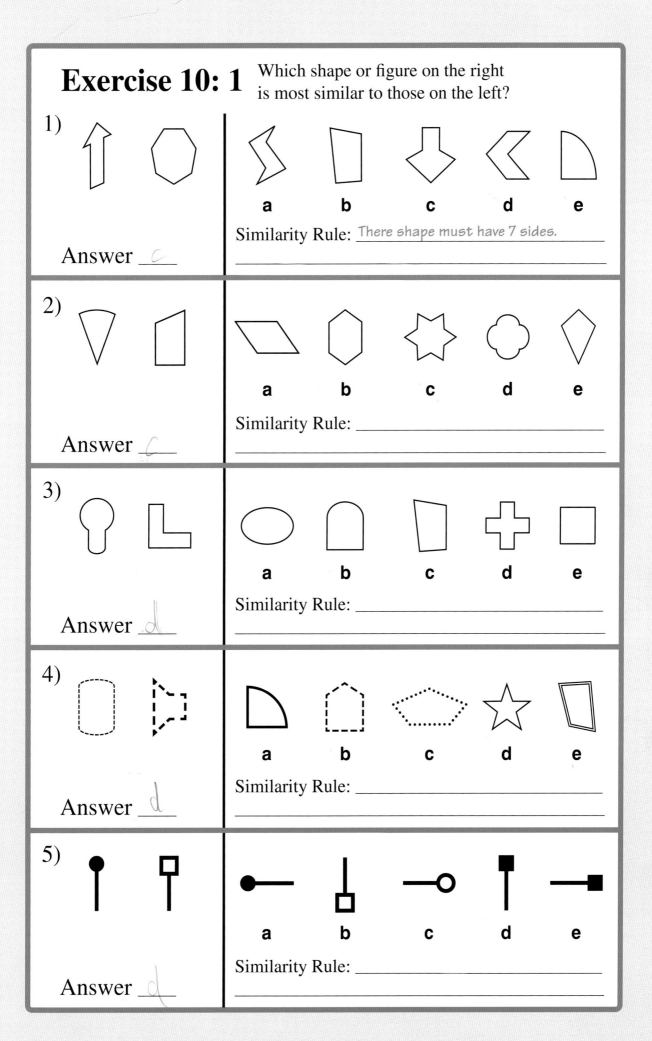

1)

Answer _c_

Similarity Rule: _There shape must have 7 sides._

2)

Answer _c_

Similarity Rule: _____

3)

Answer _d_

Similarity Rule: _____

4)

Answer _d_

Similarity Rule: _____

5)

Answer _d_

Similarity Rule: _____

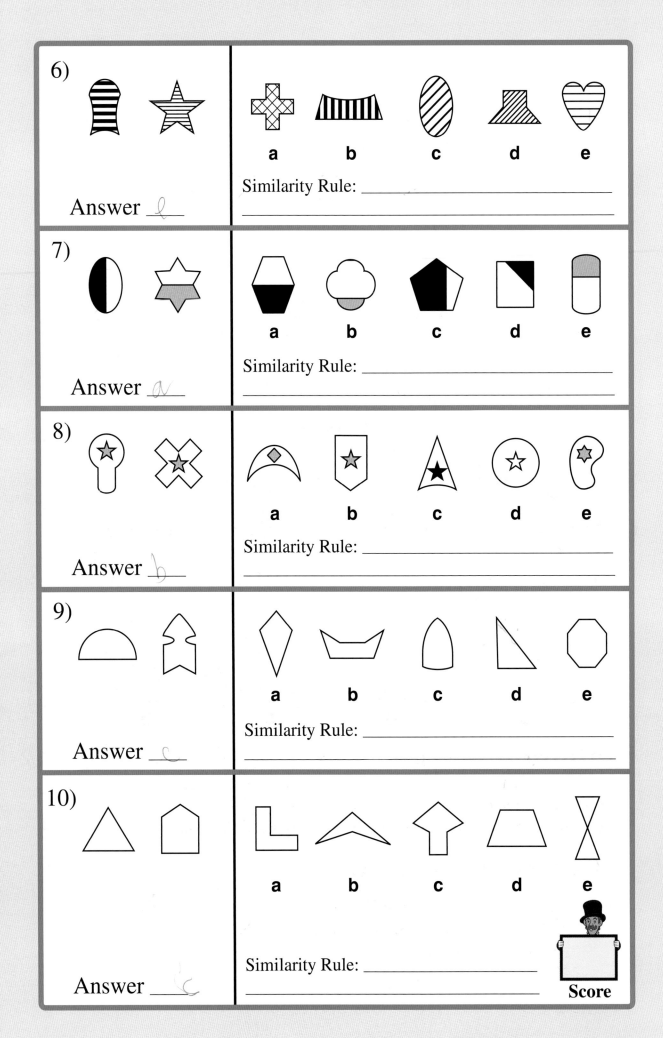

6)

Answer _e_

Similarity Rule: _____
_____

a   b   c   d   e

7)

Answer _a_

Similarity Rule: _____
_____

a   b   c   d   e

8)

Answer _b_

Similarity Rule: _____
_____

a   b   c   d   e

9)

Answer _c_

Similarity Rule: _____
_____

a   b   c   d   e

10)

Answer _c_

Similarity Rule: _____
_____

a   b   c   d   e

Score

2. Level Two

In **Level Two** similarity questions, there are two layers or similarities to look for between the figures.

Example: | Which figure on the right is most like the two figures on the left?

a　　**b**　　**c**　　**d**

The Rules of Similarity:

Layer 1 - The shapes must be identical or completely different.
Layer 2 - The shapes must be in groups of two or three.

Remember: The rules are only relevant if they help to select the right alternative and eliminate the wrong ones.

The Set of Figures:

a　　　　**b**　　　　**c**　　　　**d**

It is important to **eliminate** the wrong possibilities:
a - There are two identical shapes and one shape is different.
b - There should only be two or three shapes.
c - There are two identical shapes and one shape is different.

The Correct Figure:

This figure follows the rules of similarity.
Layer 1 - All the Triangles are identical.
Layer 2 - The Triangles are in a group of three.

Answer: **d**

Exercise 10: 2

Which figure on the right is most similar to those on the left?

1)

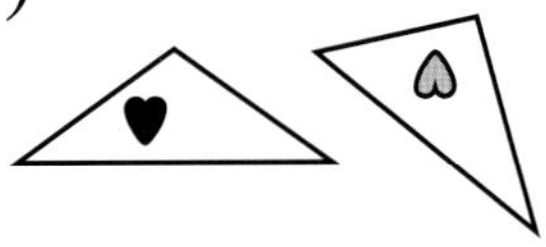

a   b   c   d   e

Similarity Rules →

Answer _a_

i) The outer shape must be a Triangle.

ii) There must be a Heart Shape with a Grey or Black Fill.

2)

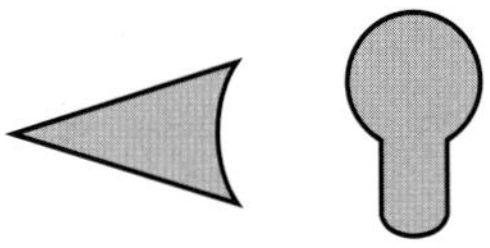

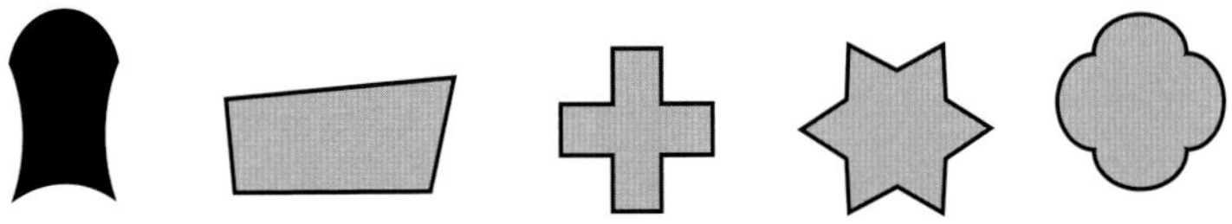

a   b   c   d   e

Similarity Rules →

Answer _e_

i) _____

ii) _____

3)

a   b   c   d   e

Similarity Rules →

Answer _a_

i) _____

ii) _____

4)

a   b   c   d   e

Similarity Rules →

Answer _b_

i) _____

ii) _____

5)

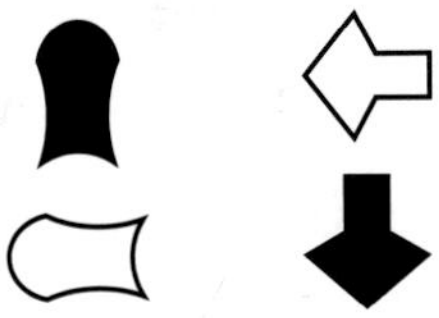

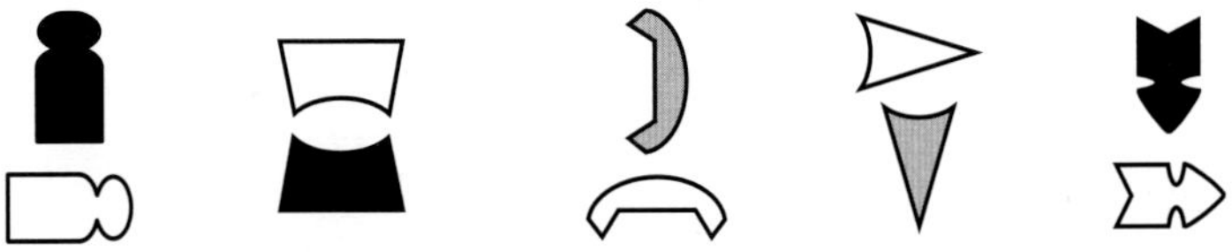

a   b   c   d   e

Similarity Rules →

Answer _b_

i) _____

ii) _____

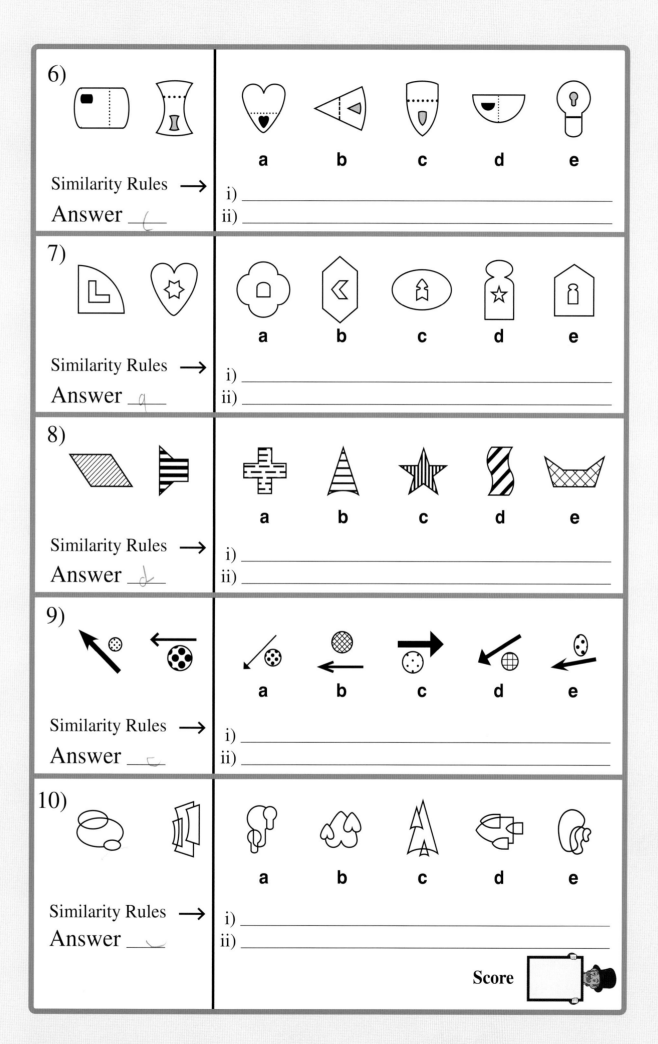

6)

a   b   c   d   e

Similarity Rules →

Answer _____

i) _____

ii) _____

7)

a   b   c   d   e

Similarity Rules →

Answer _____

i) _____

ii) _____

8)

a   b   c   d   e

Similarity Rules →

Answer _____

i) _____

ii) _____

9)

a   b   c   d   e

Similarity Rules →

Answer _____

i) _____

ii) _____

10)

a   b   c   d   e

Similarity Rules →

Answer _____

i) _____

ii) _____

Score

3. Level Three

In **Level Three** similarity questions, there are three layers or similarities to look for between the figures.

Example: | Which figure on the right is most like the two figures on the left?

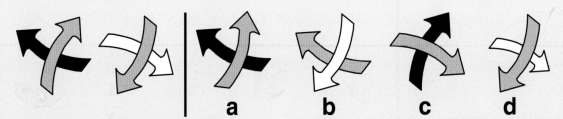

The Rules of Similarity:

Layer 1 - The Arrow Shapes are the same size.
Layer 2 - The Arrow Shape with a Grey Fill always overlays the second Arrow Shape.
Layer 3 - The two Arrow Shapes are related by rotation (a rotational difference of 90°).

Remember: The rules are only relevant if they help to select the right alternative and eliminate the wrong ones.

The Set of Figures:

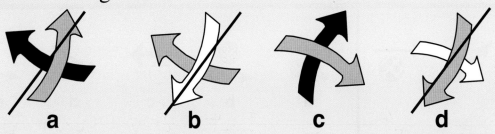

It is important to **eliminate** the wrong possibilities:

a - The Arrow Shapes are not rotations but inversions of each other.
b - The Arrow Shape with a White Fill forms the overlay.
d - The Arrow Shape with a White Fill is smaller than the other Arrow Shape.

The Correct Figure:

This figure follows the rules of similarity.
Layer 1 - Both Arrow Shapes are the same size.
Layer 2 - The Arrow Shape with a Grey Fill overlays the second Arrow Shape with a Black Fill.
Layer 3 - The two Arrow Shapes are related by rotation (a rotational difference of 90°).

Answer: **c**

Exercise 10: 3

Which figure on the right is most similar to those on the left?

1)

Similarity Rules →

Answer _b_

i) The main shape must be an Equilateral Triangle.
ii) There must be an enclosed Circle.
iii) There must be a 6-sided shape outside of the Triangle.

2)

Similarity Rules →

Answer _d_

i) _____
ii) _____
iii) _____

3)

Similarity Rules →

Answer _d_

i) _____
ii) _____
iii) _____

4)

Similarity Rules →

Answer _a_

i) _____
ii) _____
iii) _____

5)

Similarity Rules →

Answer _b_

i) _____
ii) _____
iii) _____

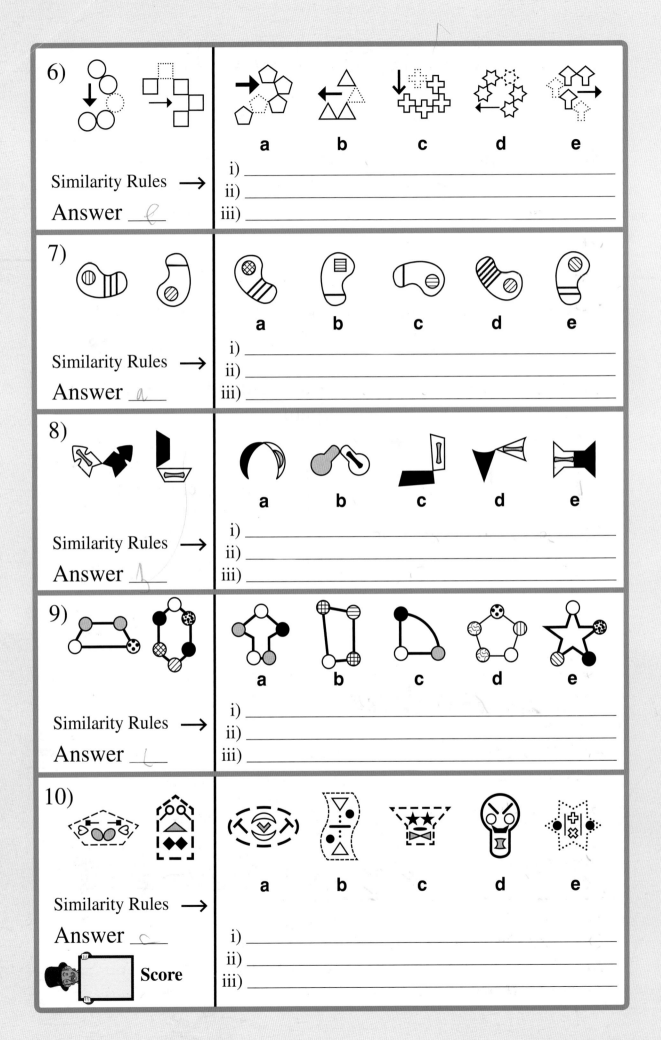

6)

a **b** **c** **d** **e**

Similarity Rules →

i) _____

ii) _____

Answer _e_

iii) _____

7)

a **b** **c** **d** **e**

Similarity Rules →

i) _____

ii) _____

Answer _a_

iii) _____

8)

a **b** **c** **d** **e**

Similarity Rules →

i) _____

ii) _____

Answer _A_

iii) _____

9)

a **b** **c** **d** **e**

Similarity Rules →

i) _____

ii) _____

Answer _L_

iii) _____

10)

a **b** **c** **d** **e**

Similarity Rules →

Answer _c_

Score

i) _____

ii) _____

iii) _____

Chapter Eleven
SERIES

Series questions in Verbal Reasoning can be either:

Letter Sequences or **Number Sequences**

Letter or number patterns can be **Repetitive** or **Cumulative**.

Repetitive - One letter is missing each time.

For example: A ^{B} C ^{D} E ^{F} G ^{H} I ^{J} K ^{L} M ^{N} O

Cumulative - The gap between the numbers gets larger.

For example: 1 $^{+2}$ 3 $^{+3}$ 6 $^{+4}$ 10 $^{+5}$ 15 $^{+6}$ 21 $^{+7}$ 28

Series questions in Non-verbal Reasoning are of two types:
Shapes can be arranged in a repetitive pattern:

 The Telegraph Poles are in a repetitive pattern of one, two, three, two, one, two, three crossbars, etc.

Shapes can be be arranged in a Cumulative Pattern:

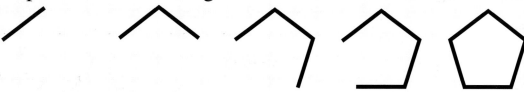

The Pentagon builds side by side in five stages.

1. Level One

In **Level One** series questions, there is only one layer or change to look for between the shapes or figures.

Example: | Which shape is missing in the series?

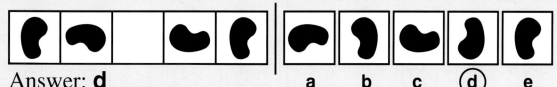

Answer: **d**   a   b   c   ⓓ   e

The Bean Shape is rotated 90° clockwise each time.

Note: In series questions, a rule only occurs if it indicates something that changes as the series progresses, e.g. we do not need to say the shape is always a Bean.

Exercise 11: 1

Which shape or figure on the right completes the series on the left?

1)

Answer d

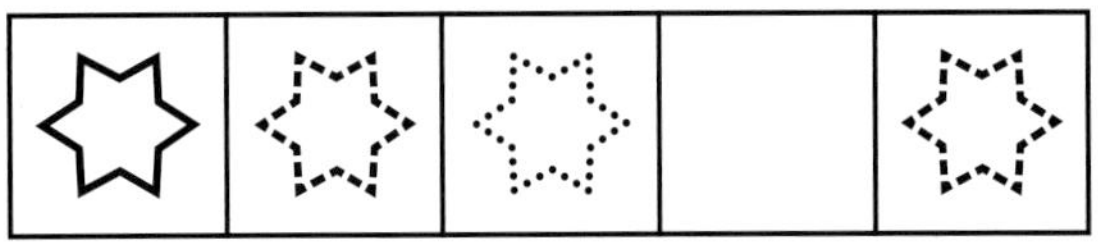

a   b   c   d   e

Series Rule:

The shape outline pattern is Solid,

Dashed, Dotted, etc.

Repetitive or Cumulative?

Repetitive

2)

Answer c

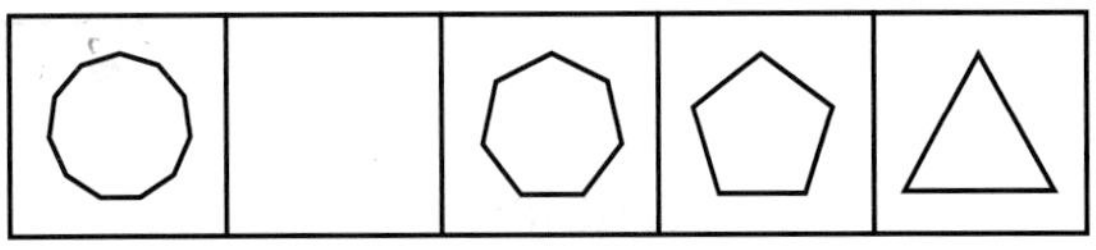

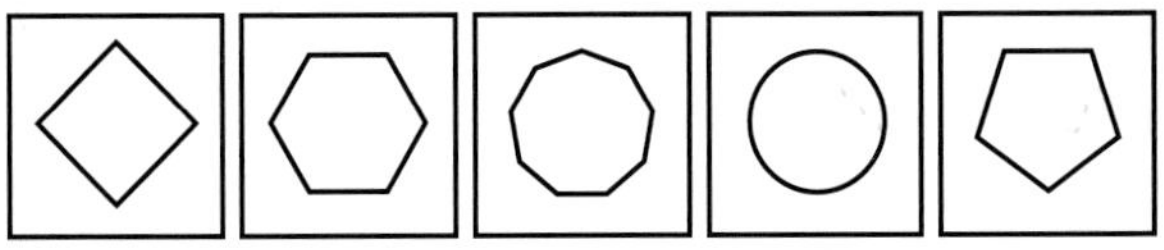

a   b   c   d   e

Series Rule:

_____

_____

Repetitive or Cumulative?

_____

3)

Answer b

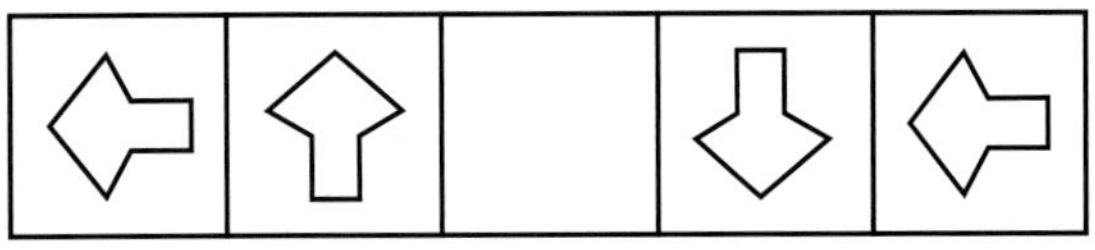

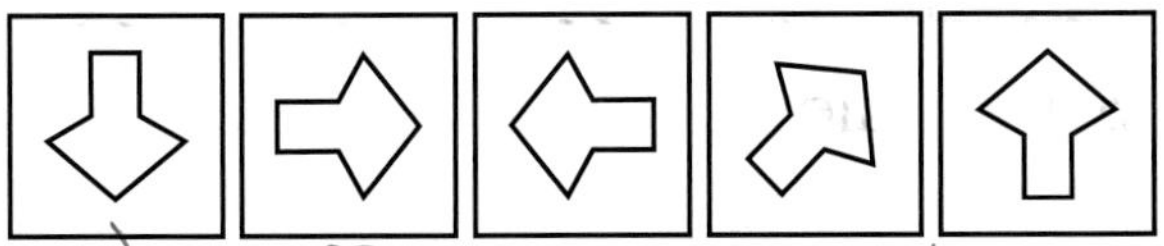

a   b   c   d   e

Series Rule:

_____

_____

Repetitive or Cumulative?

_____

4)

Answer e

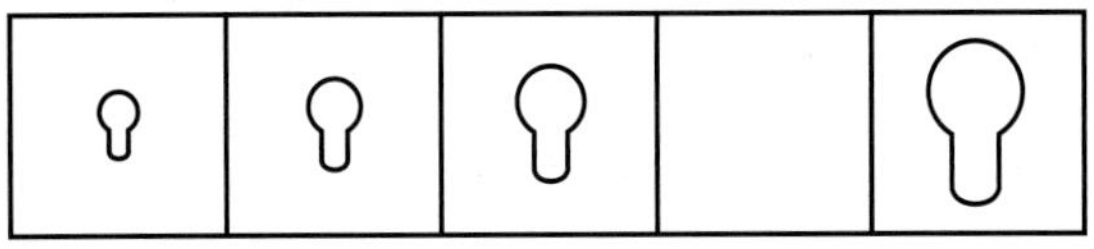

a   b   c   d   e

Series Rule:

_____

_____

Repetitive or Cumulative?

_____

5)

Answer e

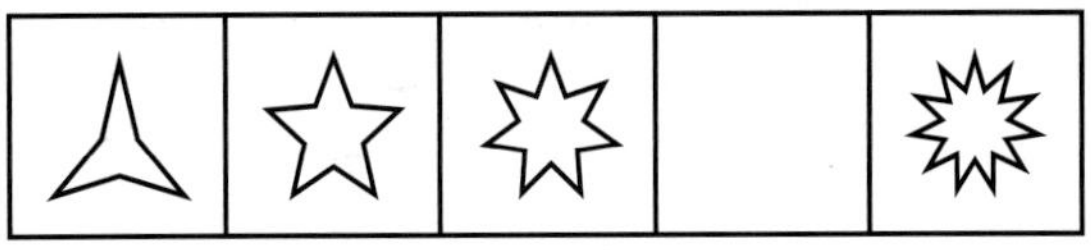

a   b   c   d   e

Series Rule:

_____

_____

Repetitive or Cumulative?

_____

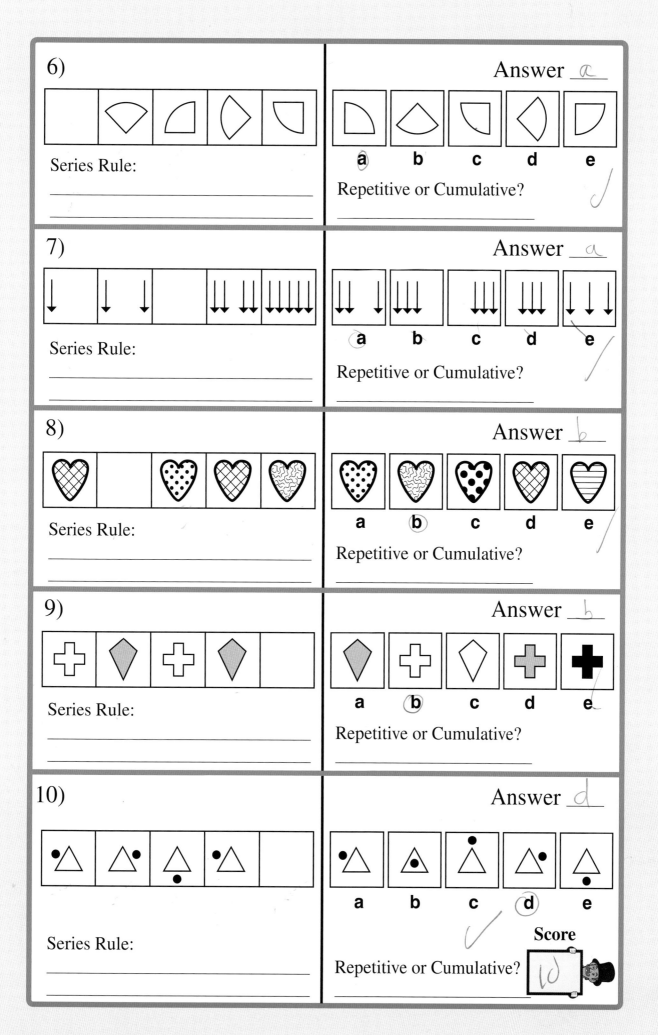

6)

Series Rule:

_____

_____

Answer __a__

a   b   c   d   e

Repetitive or Cumulative? ✓

7)

Series Rule:

_____

_____

Answer __a__

a   b   c   d   e

Repetitive or Cumulative? ✓

8)

Series Rule:

_____

_____

Answer __b__

a   b   c   d   e

Repetitive or Cumulative? ✓

9)

Series Rule:

_____

_____

Answer __b__

a   b   c   d   e

Repetitive or Cumulative?

10)

Series Rule:

_____

_____

Answer __d__

a   b   c   d   e

Repetitive or Cumulative? ✓

Score

10

2. Level Two

In **Level Two** series questions, there are two layers or changes to look for in the sequence of shapes or figures.

Example: | Which figure is missing in the series?

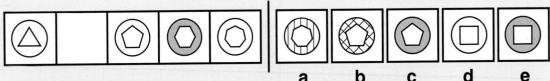
a b c d e

The Series Rules:

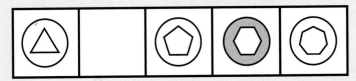

Layer 1 - The fills in the Circle alternate between White and Grey (repetitive).

Layer 2 - The frequency (number) of sides of the enclosed shape increases by one each stage (cumulative).

Remember: In series questions, a rule only occurs if it indicates something that changes as the series progresses, e.g. we do not need to say the outer shape is always a Circle.

The Set of Figures:

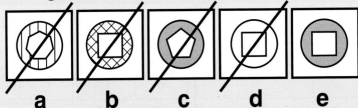
a b c d e

It is important to **eliminate** the wrong possibilities:

a - The Circle has a Shaded Fill and the enclosed shape is a Heptagon.
b - The Circle has a Cross-hatched Lattice Fill.
c - The enclosed shape is a Pentagon.
d - The Circle has a White Fill.

The Correct Figure:

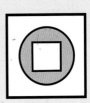

This figure follows the series rules.

Layer 1 - The fill in the Circle should be Grey (repetitive).

Layer 2 - The enclosed shape should have four sides (cumulative).

Answer: **e**

Exercise 11: 2
Which figure on the right completes the series on the left?

1)
Answer _c_

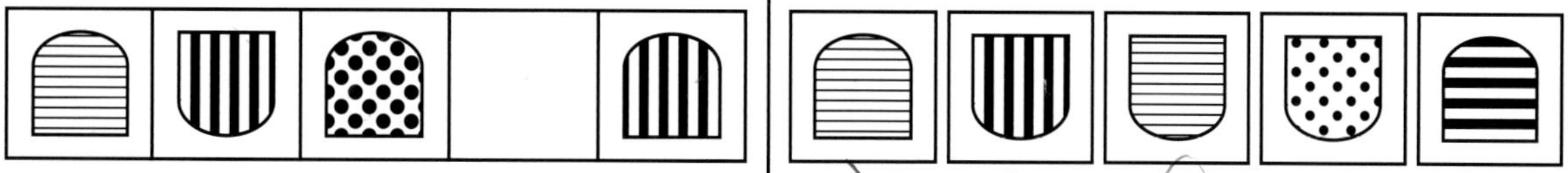

Series Rules:
i) _The Loaf Shape rotates 180° at each stage._
ii) _The fill pattern is: Horizontal Line, Vertical Line, Dotted, etc._

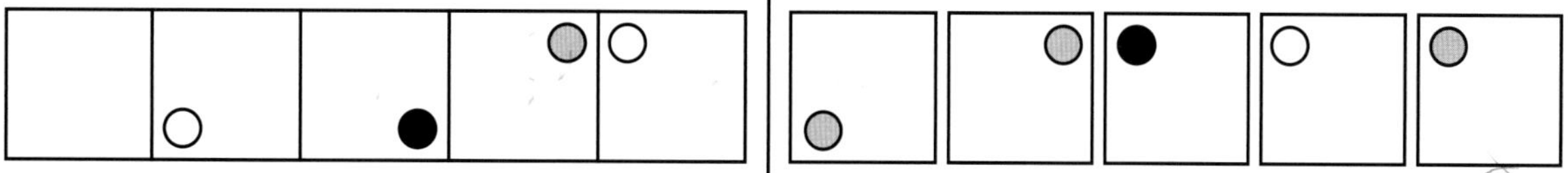

a   b   (c)   d   e

2)
Answer _e_

Series Rules:
i) _____
ii) _____

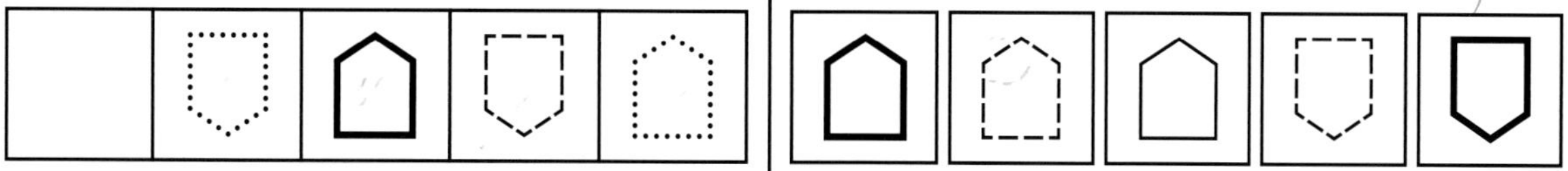

a   b   c   d   (e)

3)
Answer _a_

Series Rules:
i) _____
ii) _____

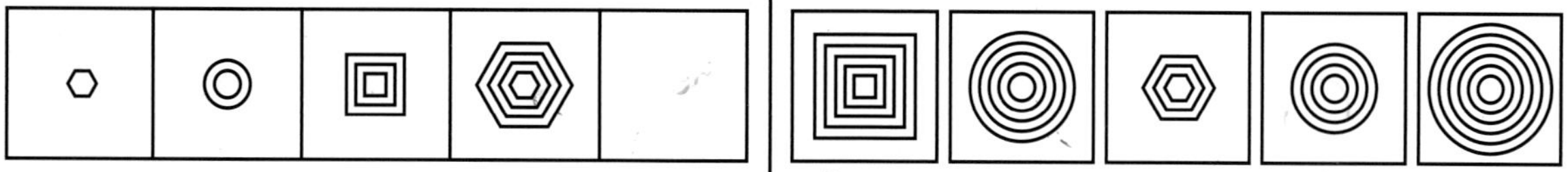

(a)   b   c   d   e

4)
Answer _b_

Series Rules:
i) _____
ii) _____

a   (b)   c   d   e

5)
Answer _b_

Series Rules:
i) _____
ii) _____

a   (b)   c   d   e

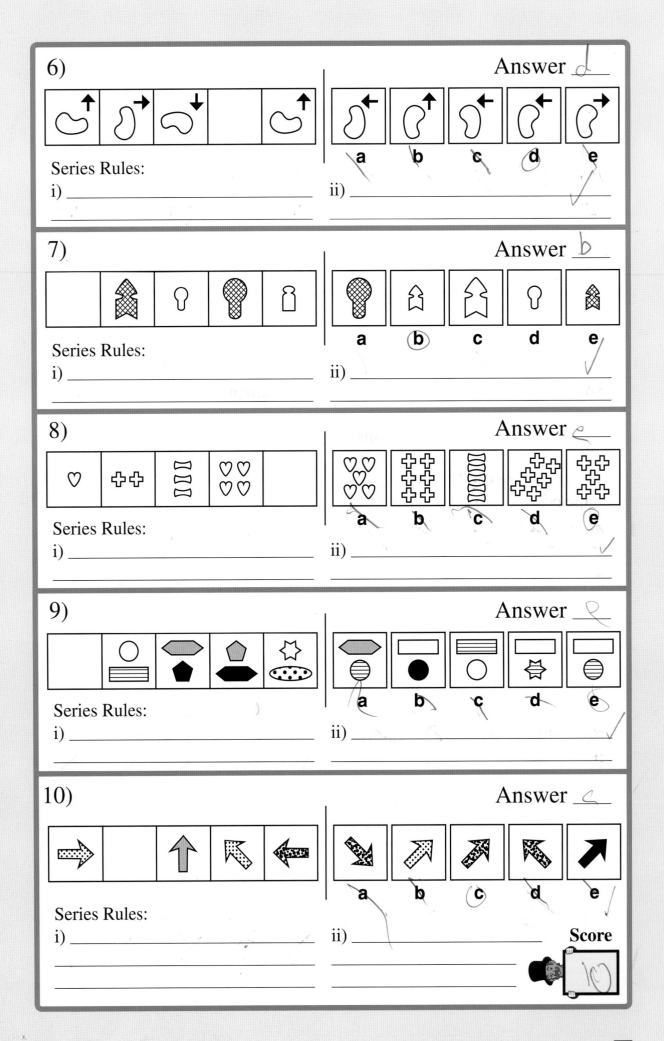

6)   Answer _d_

Series Rules:

i) _____   ii) _____

7)   Answer _b_

Series Rules:

i) _____   ii) _____

8)   Answer _e_

Series Rules:

i) _____   ii) _____

9)   Answer _e_

Series Rules:

i) _____   ii) _____

10)   Answer _c_

Series Rules:

i) _____   ii) _____

Score

40   © 2015 Stephen Curran

3. Level Three

In **Level Three** series questions, there are three layers or changes to look for in the sequence of shapes or figures.

Example: | Which figure is missing in the series?

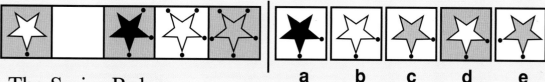

The Series Rules:

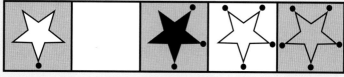

Layer 1 - The background fills in the squares alternate between Grey and White (repetitive pattern).

Layer 2 - The fills in the Star Shape go from White to Grey to Black to White, etc. (repetitive pattern).

Layer 3 - One Circle with a Black Fill is added at each stage in an anticlockwise direction around the Star Shape (cumulative pattern).

Remember: In series questions, a rule only occurs if it indicates something that changes as the series progresses, e.g. we do not need to say the main shape is always a Star.

The Set of Figures:

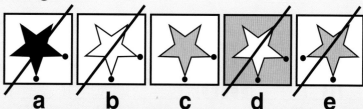

It is important to **eliminate** the wrong possibilities:

a - The Star Shape has a Black Fill.
b - The Star Shape has a White Fill.
d - The background Fill is Grey and the Star Shape has a White Fill.
e - One Circle has been added in a clockwise direction.

The Correct Figure:

This figure follows the series rules.

Layer 1 - The background fill is White (repetitive).
Layer 2 - The Star Shape has a Grey Fill (repetitive).
Layer 3 - One Circle has been added in an anticlockwise direction around the shape (cumulative).

Answer: **c**

Exercise 11: 3

Which figure on the right completes the series on the left?

a b c d e

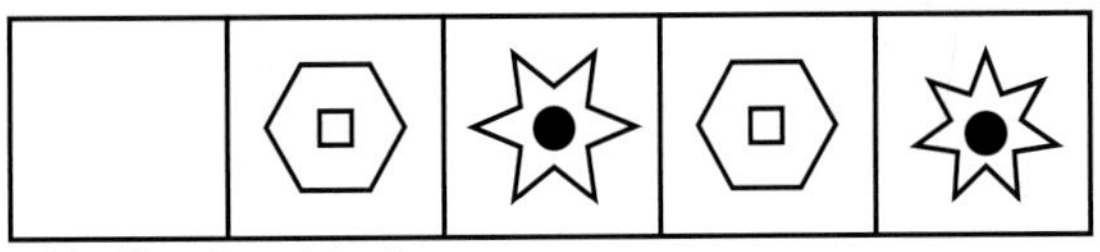

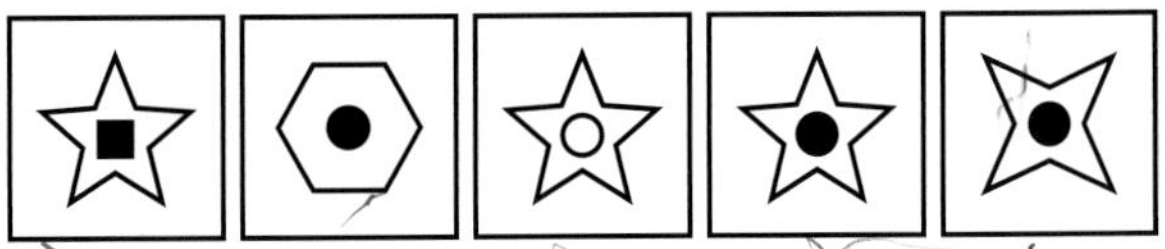

1) Series Rules:

i) Stars enclose a Black Fill Circle and Hexagons enclose a White Fill Square.

ii) The outside shape order is Star, Hexagon, Star, etc.

iii) One more point is added to the Star each time.

Answer c

a b c d e

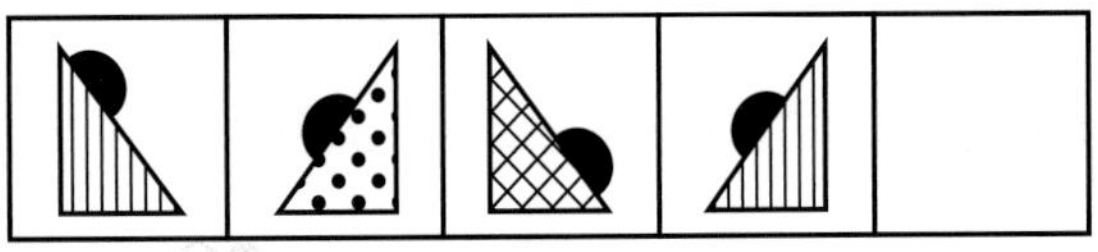

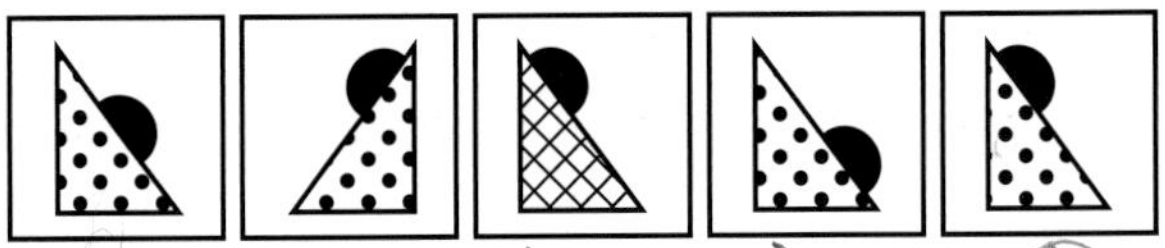

2) Series Rules:

i) ______

ii) ______

iii) ______

Answer e

a b c d e

3) Series Rules:

i) ______

ii) ______

iii) ______

Answer e

a b c d e

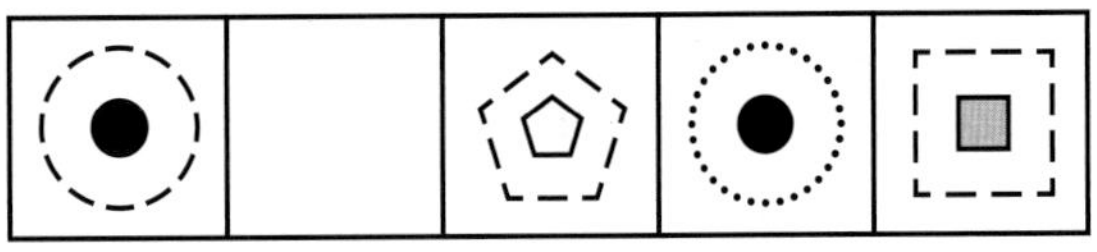

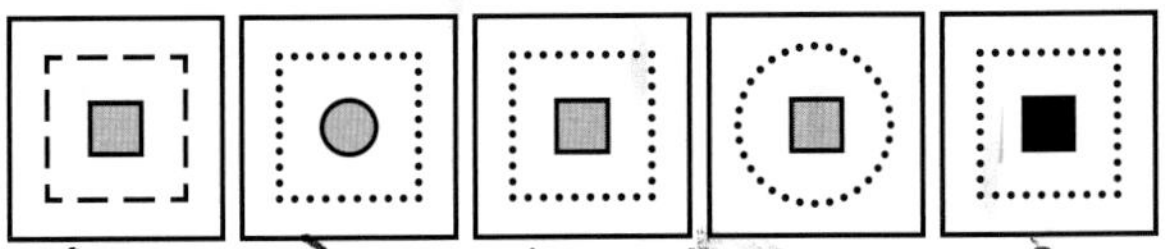

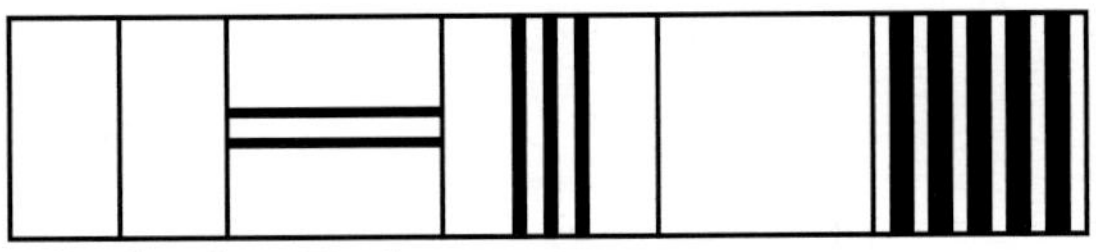

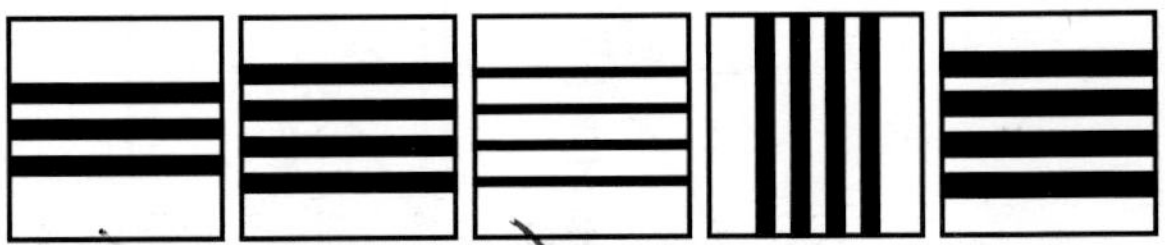

4) Series Rules:

i) ______

ii) ______

iii) ______

Answer e

a b c d e

5) Series Rules:

i) ______

ii) ______

iii) ______

Answer c

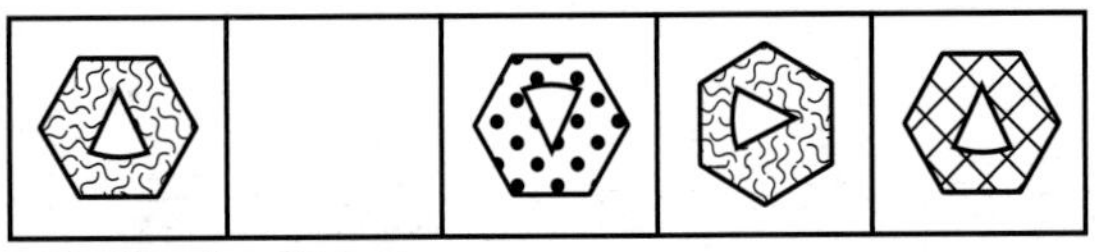

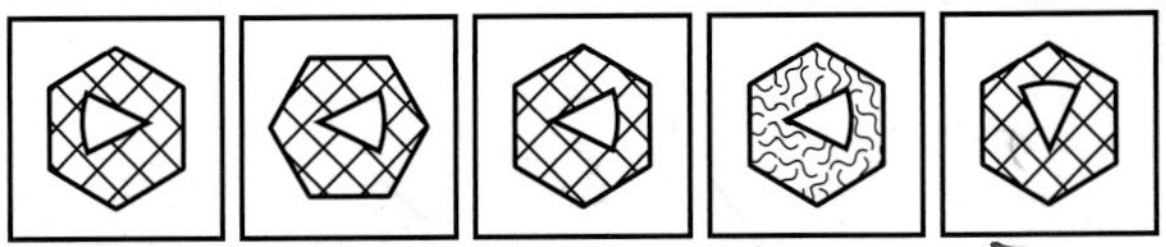

Chapter Eleven
SERIES

Series questions in Verbal Reasoning can be either:

Letter Sequences or **Number Sequences**

Letter or number patterns can be **Repetitive** or **Cumulative**.

Repetitive - One letter is missing each time.

For example: A ^{B} C ^{D} E ^{F} G ^{H} I ^{J} K ^{L} M ^{N} O

Cumulative - The gap between the numbers gets larger.

For example: 1 $^{+2}$ 3 $^{+3}$ 6 $^{+4}$ 10 $^{+5}$ 15 $^{+6}$ 21 $^{+7}$ 28

Series questions in Non-verbal Reasoning are of two types:
Shapes can be arranged in a repetitive pattern:

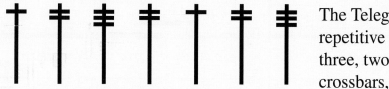

The Telegraph Poles are in a repetitive pattern of one, two, three, two, one, two, three crossbars, etc.

Shapes can be be arranged in a Cumulative Pattern:

The Pentagon builds side by side in five stages.

1. Level One

In **Level One** series questions, there is only one layer or change to look for between the shapes or figures.

Example: | Which shape is missing in the series?

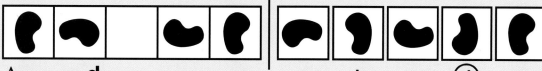

Answer: **d**   **a**   **b**   **c**   ⓓ   **e**

The Bean Shape is rotated 90° clockwise each time.

Note: In series questions, a rule only occurs if it indicates something that changes as the series progresses, e.g. we do not need to say the shape is always a Bean.

Exercise 11: 1

Which shape or figure on the right completes the series on the left?

1)

Answer *d* ✓

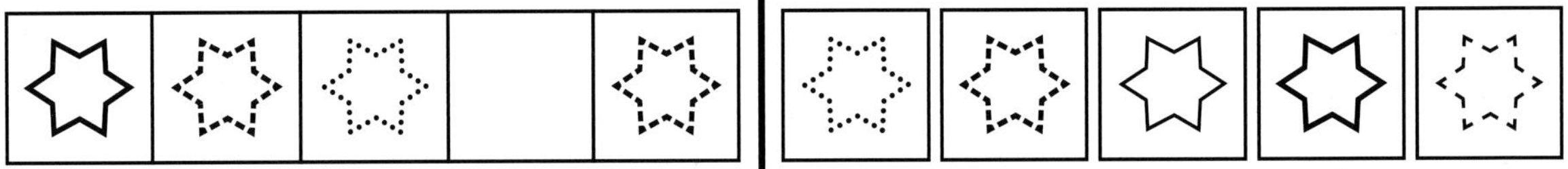

a   b   c   d   e

Series Rule:
The shape outline pattern is Solid, Dashed, Dotted, etc.

Repetitive or Cumulative?
Repetitive

2)

Answer *c*

a   b   c   d   e

Series Rule:
_____
_____

Repetitive or Cumulative?
_____ ✓

3)

Answer *b*

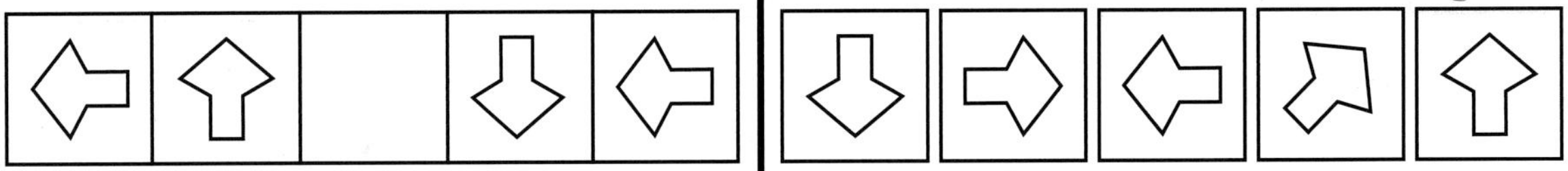

a   b   c   d   e

Series Rule:
_____
_____

Repetitive or Cumulative?
_____ ✓

4)

Answer *e*

a   b   c   d   e

Series Rule:
_____
_____

Repetitive or Cumulative?
_____ ✓

5)

Answer *e*

a   b   c   d   e

Series Rule:
_____
_____

Repetitive or Cumulative?
_____ ✓

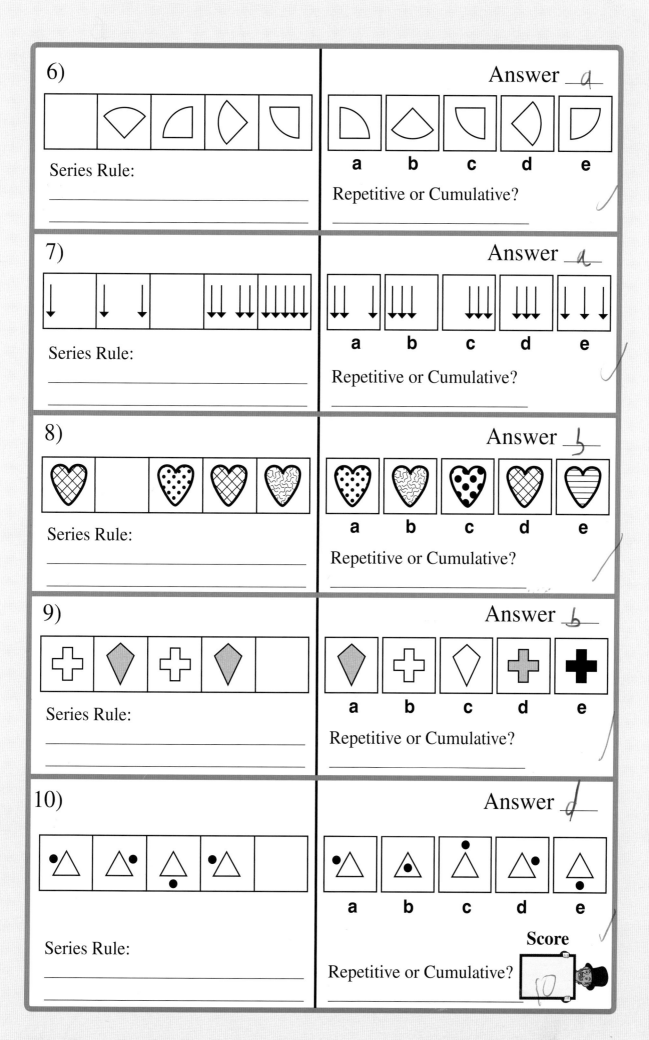

6)   Answer __a__

Series Rule:
_____
_____

a   b   c   d   e

Repetitive or Cumulative?
_____

7)   Answer __a__

Series Rule:
_____
_____

a   b   c   d   e

Repetitive or Cumulative?
_____

8)   Answer __b__

Series Rule:
_____
_____

a   b   c   d   e

Repetitive or Cumulative?
_____

9)   Answer __b__

Series Rule:
_____
_____

a   b   c   d   e

Repetitive or Cumulative?
_____

10)   Answer __d__

Series Rule:
_____
_____

a   b   c   d   e

Score

Repetitive or Cumulative?   10

37

2. Level Two

In **Level Two** series questions, there are two layers or changes to look for in the sequence of shapes or figures.

Example: | Which figure is missing in the series? |

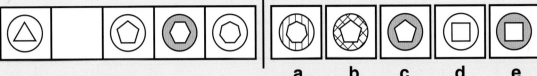

The Series Rules:

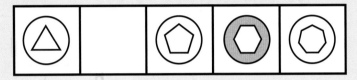

Layer 1 - The fills in the Circle alternate between White and Grey (repetitive).

Layer 2 - The frequency (number) of sides of the enclosed shape increases by one each stage (cumulative).

Remember: In series questions, a rule only occurs if it indicates something that changes as the series progresses, e.g. we do not need to say the outer shape is always a Circle.

The Set of Figures:

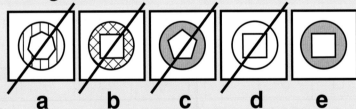

It is important to **eliminate** the wrong possibilities:

a - The Circle has a Shaded Fill and the enclosed shape is a Heptagon.

b - The Circle has a Cross-hatched Lattice Fill.

c - The enclosed shape is a Pentagon.

d - The Circle has a White Fill.

The Correct Figure:

This figure follows the series rules.

Layer 1 - The fill in the Circle should be Grey (repetitive).

Layer 2 - The enclosed shape should have four sides (cumulative).

Answer: **e**

Exercise 11: 2

Which figure on the right completes the series on the left?

1) Answer c

a b c d e

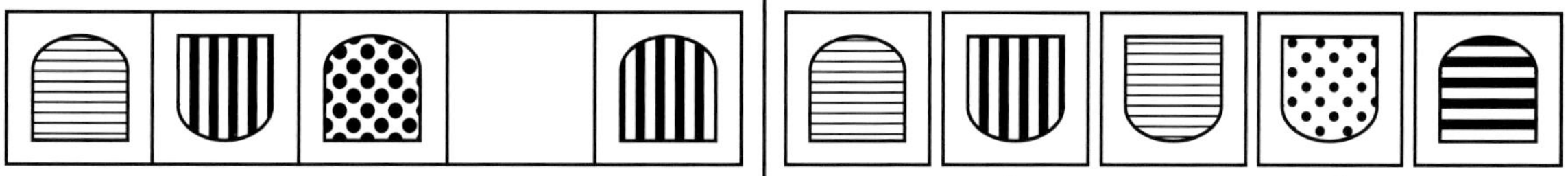

Series Rules:

i) The Loaf Shape rotates 180° at each stage.

ii) The fill pattern is: Horizontal Line, Vertical Line, Dotted, etc.

2) Answer e

a b c d e

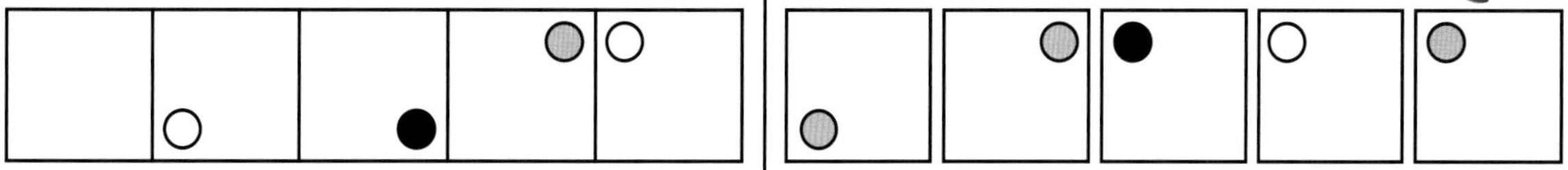

Series Rules:

i) ______________________

ii) ______________________

3) Answer a

a b c d e

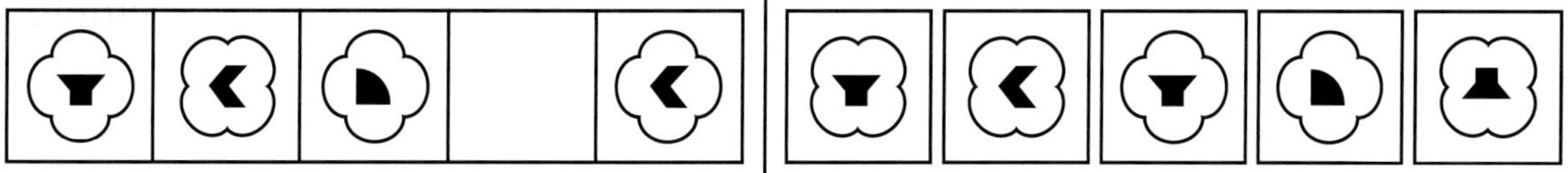

Series Rules:

i) ______________________

ii) ______________________

4) Answer b

a b c d e

Series Rules:

i) ______________________

ii) ______________________

5) Answer b

a b c d e

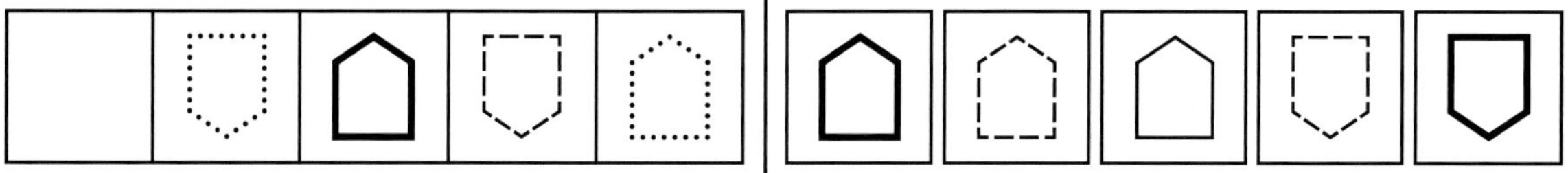

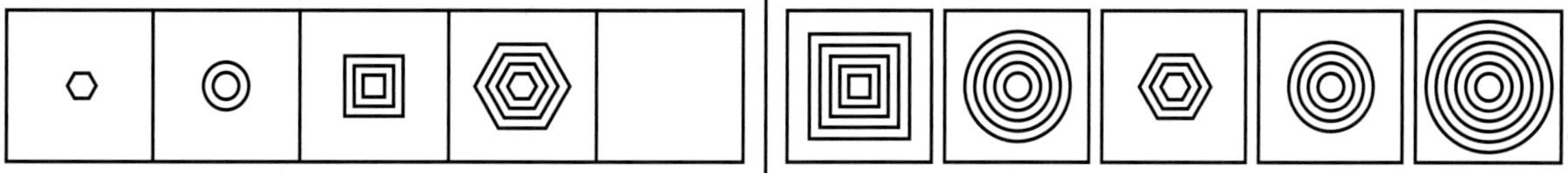

Series Rules:

i) ______________________

ii) ______________________

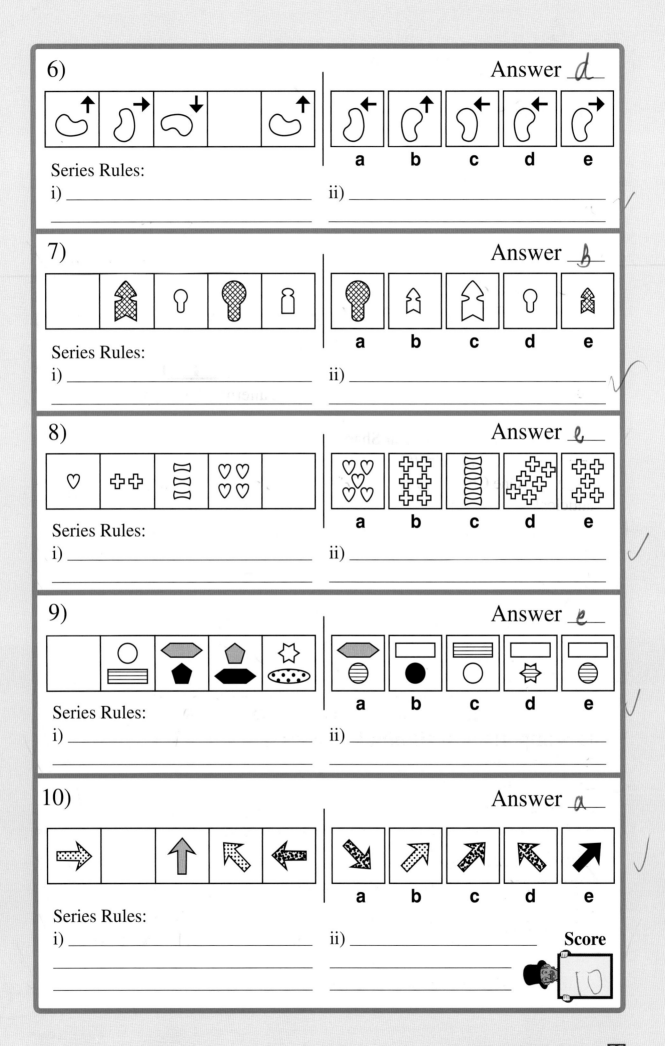

6)   Answer _d_

Series Rules:

i) _____   ii) _____

_____

7)   Answer _b_

Series Rules:

i) _____   ii) _____

_____

8)   Answer _e_

Series Rules:

i) _____   ii) _____

_____

9)   Answer _e_

Series Rules:

i) _____   ii) _____

_____

10)   Answer _a_

Series Rules:

i) _____   ii) _____   **Score**

_____   _____

© 2015 Stephen Curran

3. Level Three

In **Level Three** series questions, there are three layers or changes to look for in the sequence of shapes or figures.

Example: | Which figure is missing in the series?

The Series Rules:

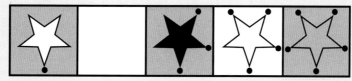

Layer 1 - The background fills in the squares alternate between Grey and White (repetitive pattern).

Layer 2 - The fills in the Star Shape go from White to Grey to Black to White, etc. (repetitive pattern).

Layer 3 - One Circle with a Black Fill is added at each stage in an anticlockwise direction around the Star Shape (cumulative pattern).

Remember: In series questions, a rule only occurs if it indicates something that changes as the series progresses, e.g. we do not need to say the main shape is always a Star.

The Set of Figures:

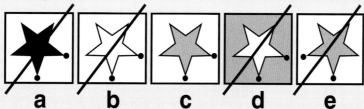

It is important to **eliminate** the wrong possibilities:

a - The Star Shape has a Black Fill.
b - The Star Shape has a White Fill.
d - The background Fill is Grey and the Star Shape has a White Fill.
e - One Circle has been added in a clockwise direction.

The Correct Figure:

This figure follows the series rules.

Layer 1 - The background fill is White (repetitive).
Layer 2 - The Star Shape has a Grey Fill (repetitive).
Layer 3 - One Circle has been added in an anticlockwise direction around the shape (cumulative).

Answer: **c**

Exercise 11: 3

Which figure on the right completes the series on the left?

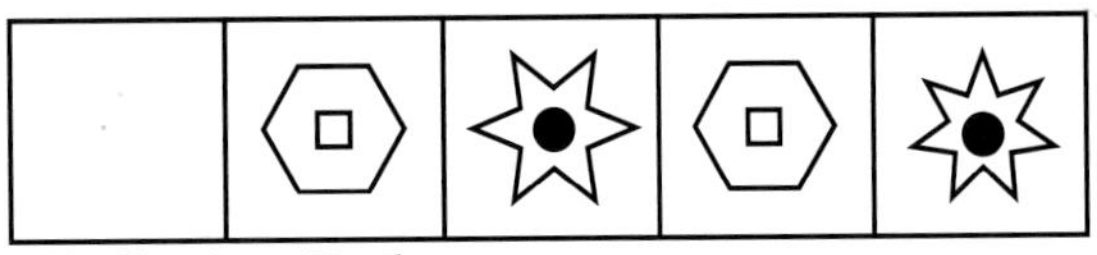

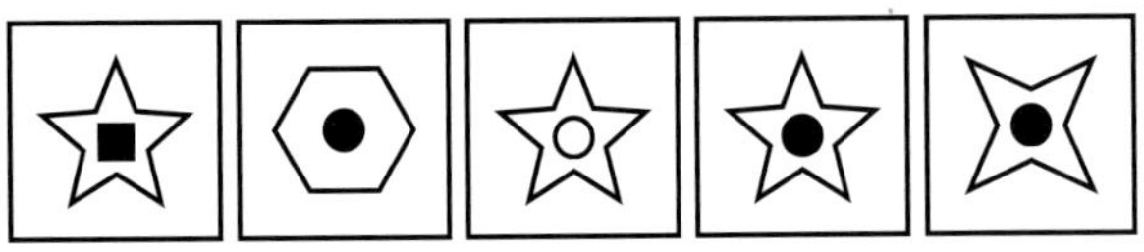

a b c d e

1) Series Rules:

i) Stars enclose a Black Fill Circle and Hexagons enclose a White Fill Square.

ii) The outside shape order is Star, Hexagon, Star, etc.

Answer d

iii) One more point is added to the Star each time.

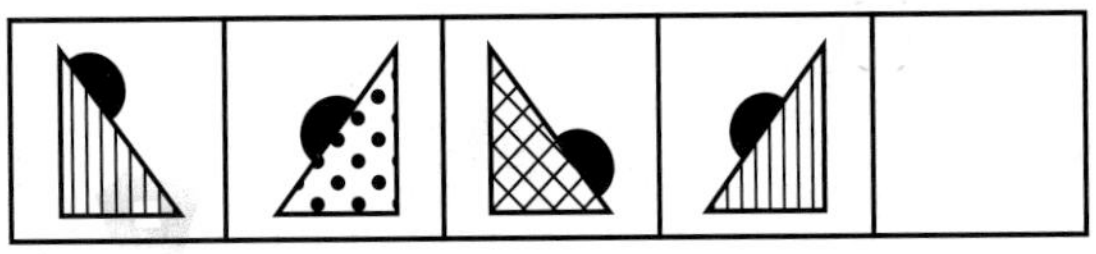

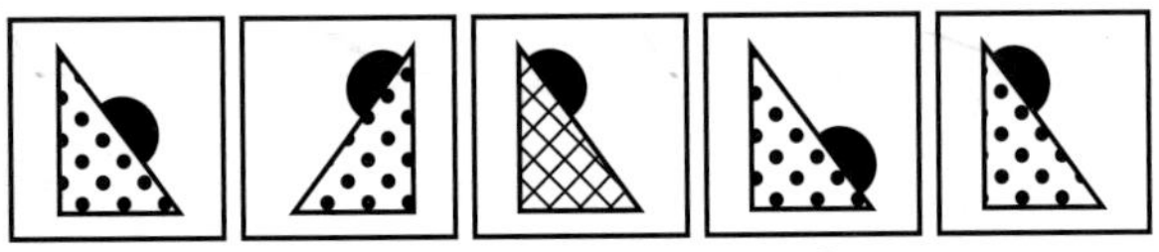

a b c d e

2) Series Rules:

i) ______

ii) ______

Answer e

iii) ______

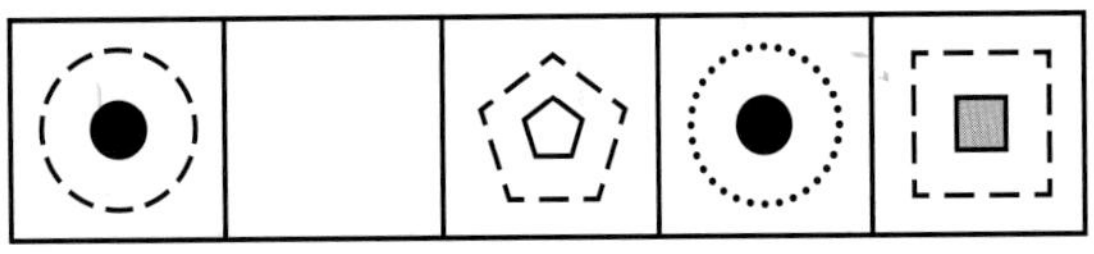

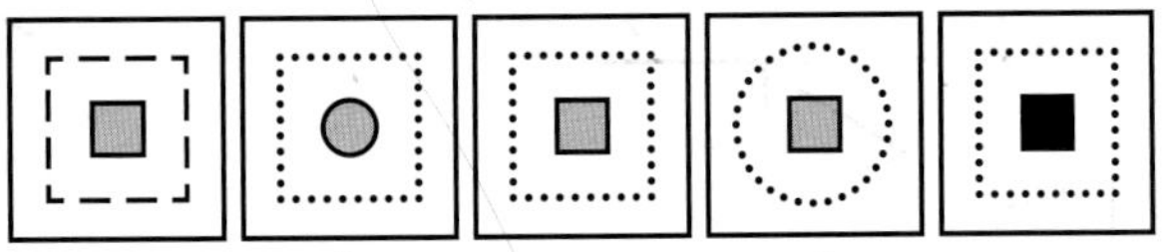

a b c d e

3) Series Rules:

i) ______

ii) ______

Answer e

iii) ______

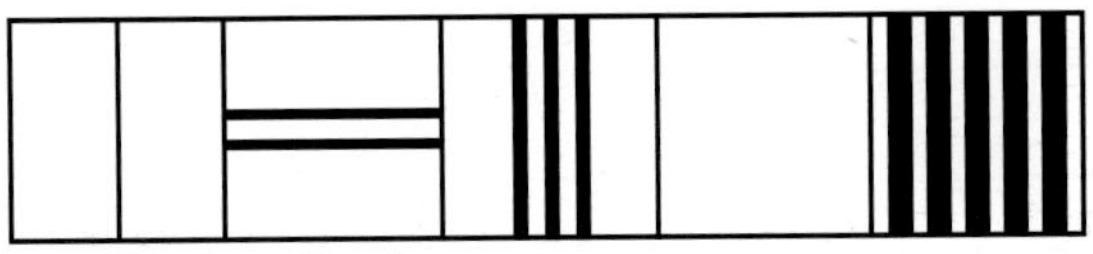

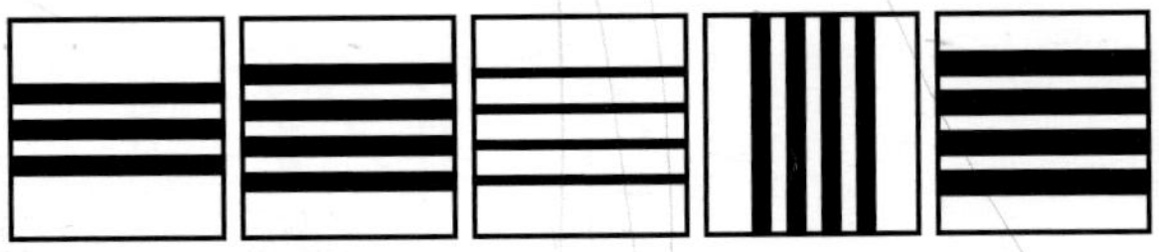

a b c d e

4) Series Rules:

i) ______

ii) ______

Answer c

iii) ______

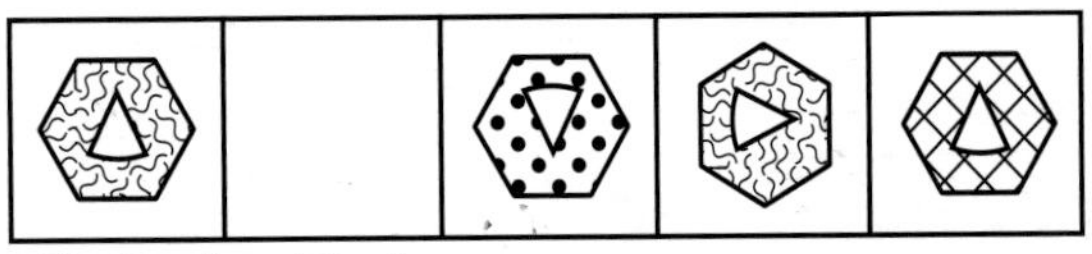

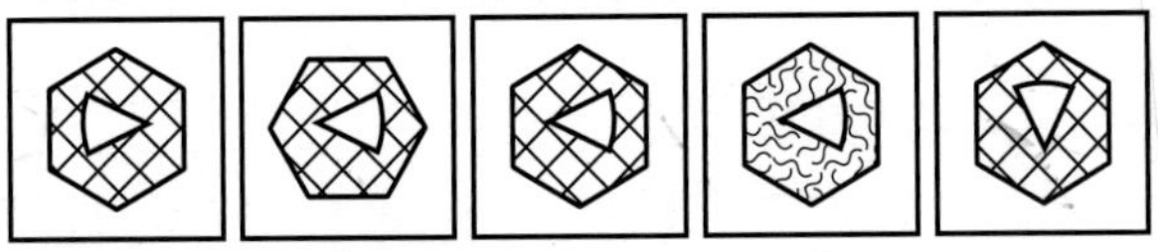

a b c d e

5) Series Rules:

i) ______

ii) ______

Answer c

iii) ______

Exercise 12: 3

Which shape or figure on the right completes the matrix?

Note: If the shapes in a row or column are of the same type, establish the rules in that direction.

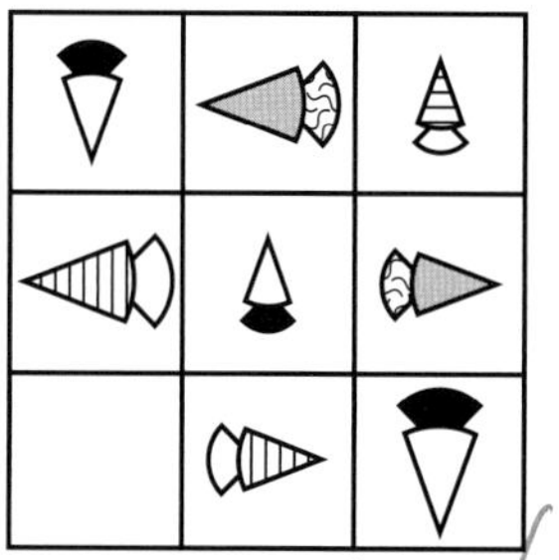

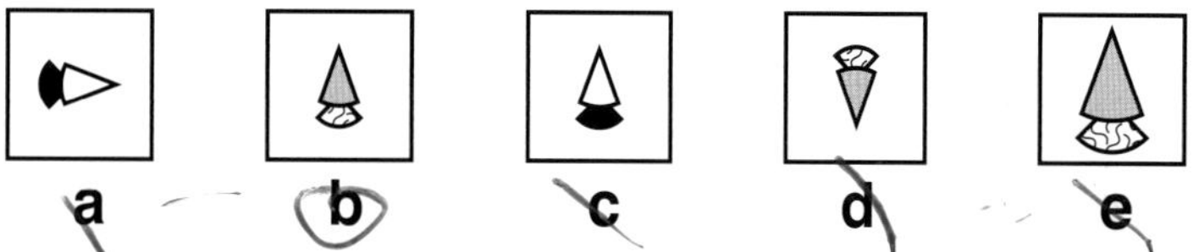

a   b   c   d   e

1) Matrix Rules: This can be solved in either direction.

i) *The figure rotates 90° clockwise at each stage.*

ii) *Each row has one of each figure.*

iii) *Each row has a small, medium and large figure.*

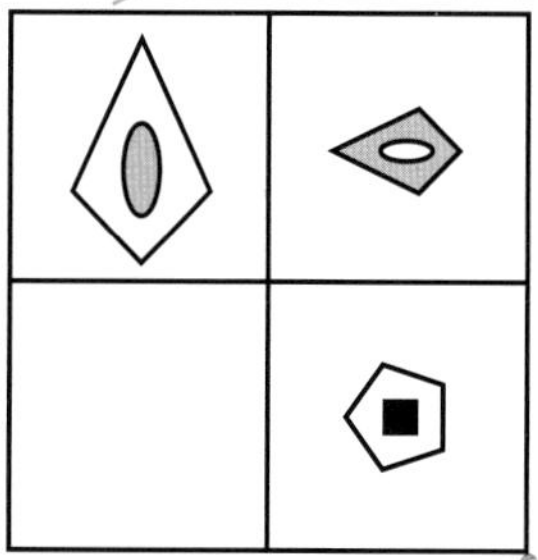

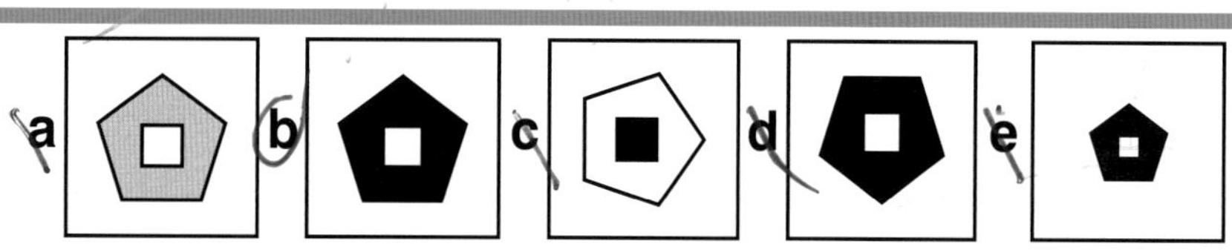

Answer **b**

---

a   b   c   d   e

2) Matrix Rules: This matrix is best solved **horizontally** .

i) _____

ii) _____

iii) _____

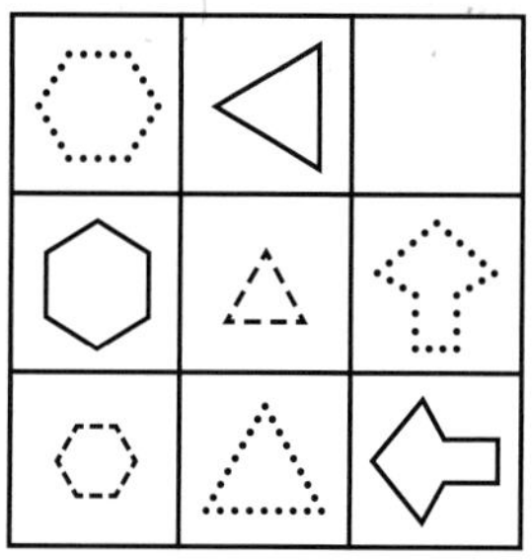

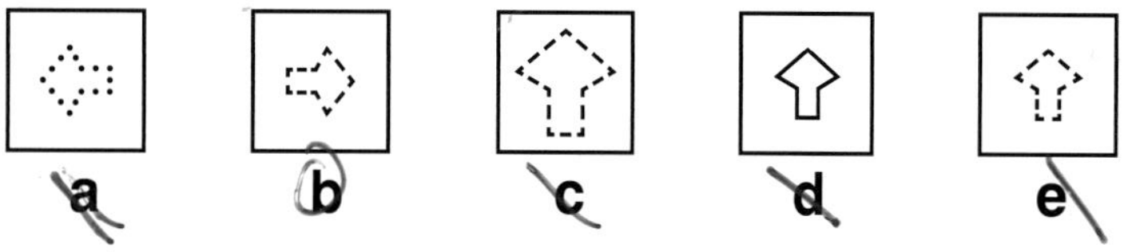

Answer **b**

---

a   b   c   d   e

3) Matrix Rules: This matrix is best solved _____ .

i) _____

ii) _____

iii) _____

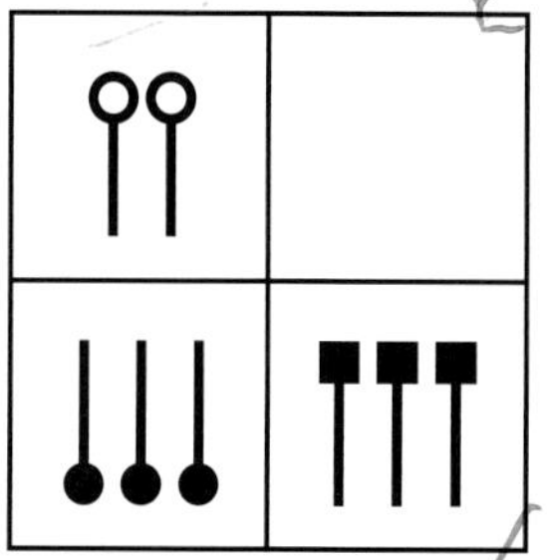

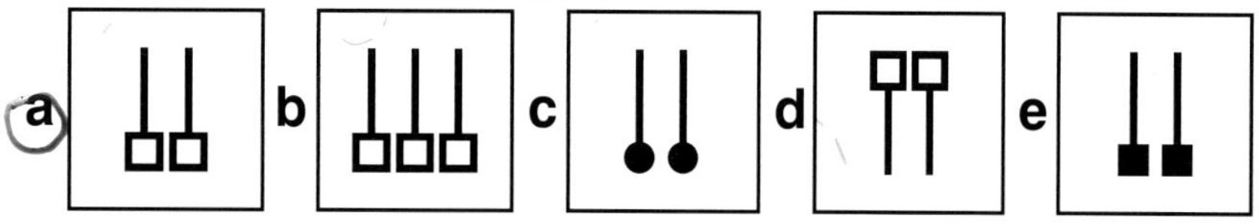

Answer **b**

---

a   b   c   d   e

4) Matrix Rules: This matrix is best solved _____ .

i) _____

ii) _____

iii) _____

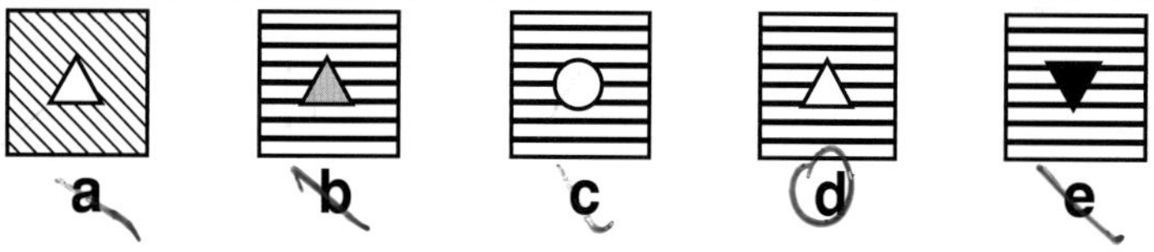

Answer **a**

---

a   b   c   d   e

5) Matrix Rules: This can be solved in either direction.

i) _____

ii) _____

iii) _____

Answer **d**

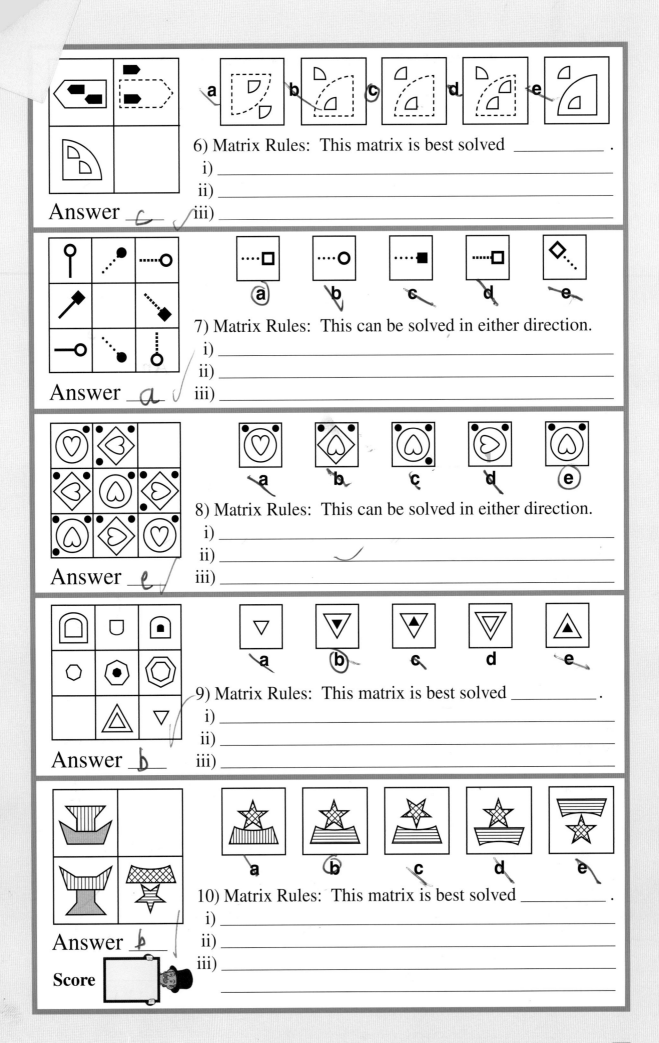

6) Matrix Rules: This matrix is best solved _____ .
i) _____
ii) _____
Answer _c_ iii) _____

7) Matrix Rules: This can be solved in either direction.
i) _____
ii) _____
Answer _a_ iii) _____

8) Matrix Rules: This can be solved in either direction.
i) _____
ii) _____
Answer _e_ iii) _____

9) Matrix Rules: This matrix is best solved _____ .
i) _____
ii) _____
Answer _b_ iii) _____

10) Matrix Rules: This matrix is best solved _____ .
i) _____
ii) _____
Answer _b_ iii) _____

Score

Chapter Thirteen
REVISION
1. Odd One Out

Exercise 13: 1a   Which figure is the odd one out?

1)

a   b   c   d   e

Answer ____

2)

a   b   c   d   e

Answer ____

3)

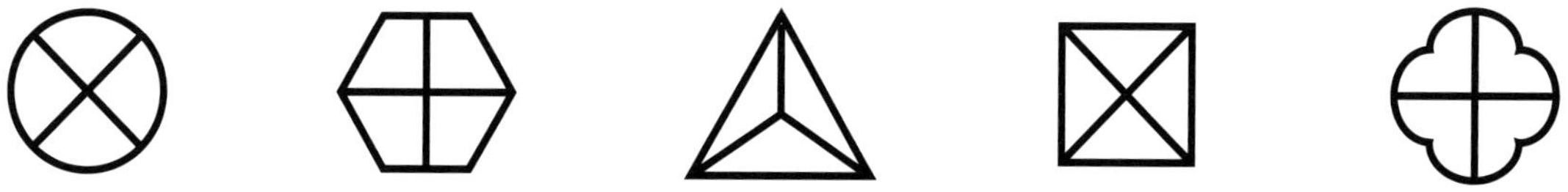

a   b   c   d   e

Answer ____

4)

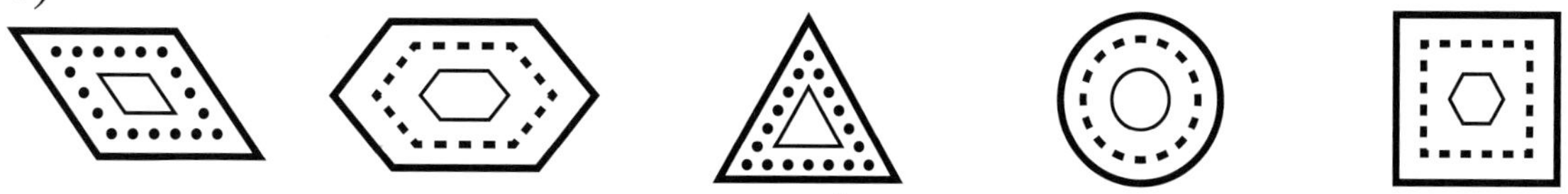

a   b   c   d   e

Answer ____

5)

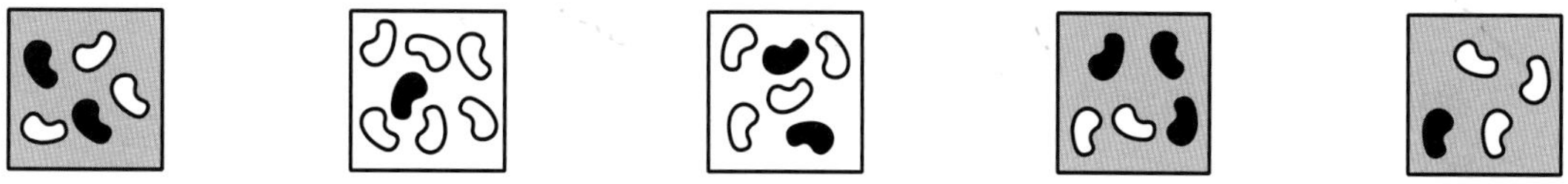

a   b   c   d   e

Answer ____

2. Codes

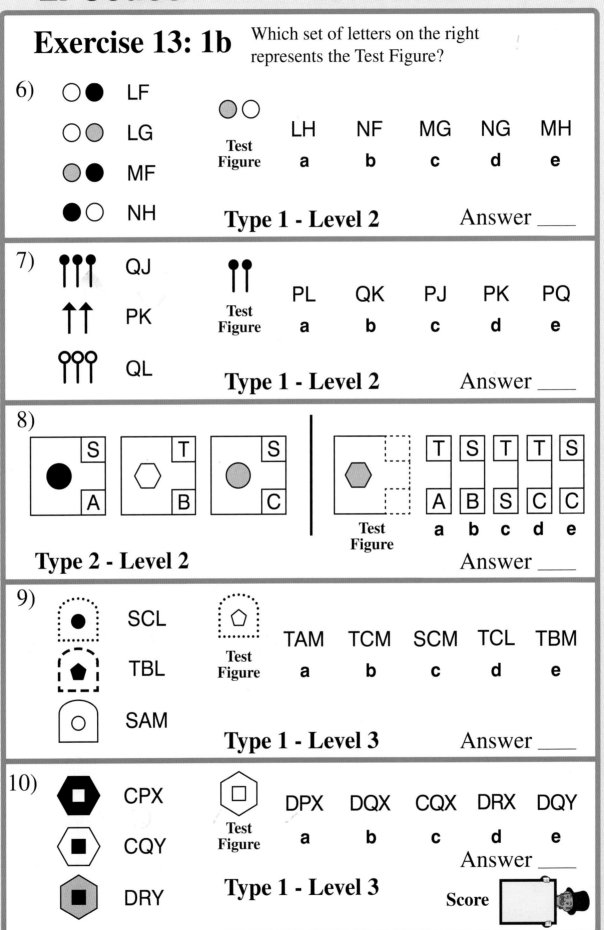

Exercise 13: 1b
Which set of letters on the right represents the Test Figure?

6)

○●	LF
○◐	LG
◐●	MF
●○	NH

Test Figure: ◐○

	LH	NF	MG	NG	MH
	a	**b**	**c**	**d**	**e**

Type 1 - Level 2   Answer ____

7)

♀♀♀	QJ
↑↑	PK
♀♀♀	QL

Test Figure: ♀♀

	PL	QK	PJ	PK	PQ
	a	**b**	**c**	**d**	**e**

Type 1 - Level 2   Answer ____

8)

Type 2 - Level 2

Test Figure

T	S	T	T	S
A	B	S	C	C
a	**b**	**c**	**d**	**e**

Answer ____

9)

⦿	SCL
⬠	TBL
⌂	SAM

Test Figure

	TAM	TCM	SCM	TCL	TBM
	a	**b**	**c**	**d**	**e**

Type 1 - Level 3   Answer ____

10)

⬡	CPX
⬡	CQY
⬡	DRY

Test Figure

DPX	DQX	CQX	DRX	DQY
a	**b**	**c**	**d**	**e**

Answer ____

Type 1 - Level 3   Score ☐

3. Analogies

Exercise 13: 2a

Which shape or figure completes the analogy?

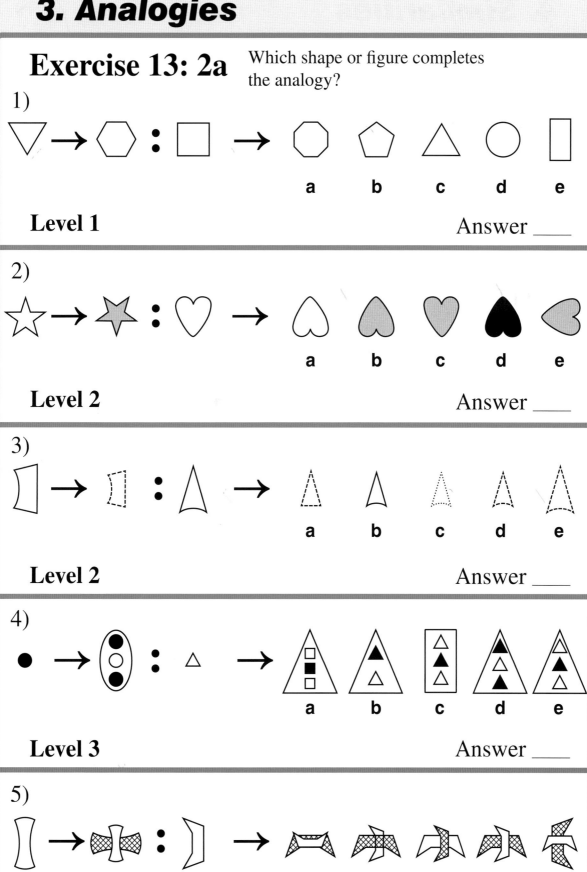

1)

                  a   b   c   d   e

Level 1   Answer ____

2)

                  a   b   c   d   e

Level 2   Answer ____

3)

                  a   b   c   d   e

Level 2   Answer ____

4)

                  a   b   c   d   e

Level 3   Answer ____

5)

                  a   b   c   d   e

Level 3   Answer ____

4. Similarities

Exercise 13: 2b

Which figure on the right is most similar to those on the left?

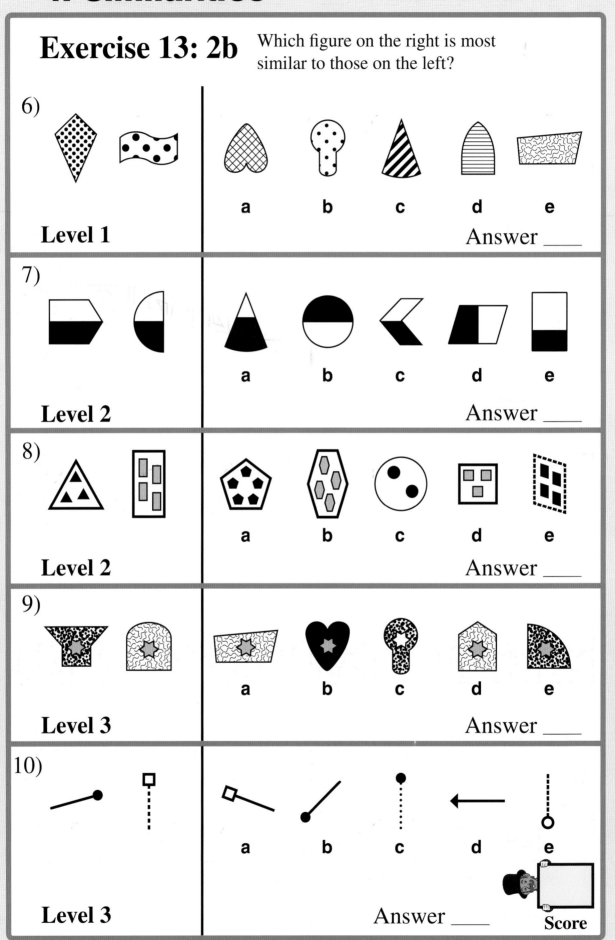

6) **Level 1**

a   b   c   d   e

Answer ____

7) **Level 2**

a   b   c   d   e

Answer ____

8) **Level 2**

a   b   c   d   e

Answer ____

9) **Level 3**

a   b   c   d   e

Answer ____

10) **Level 3**

a   b   c   d   e

Answer ____

Score

5. Series

Exercise 13: 3a

Which shape or figure on the right completes the series on the left?

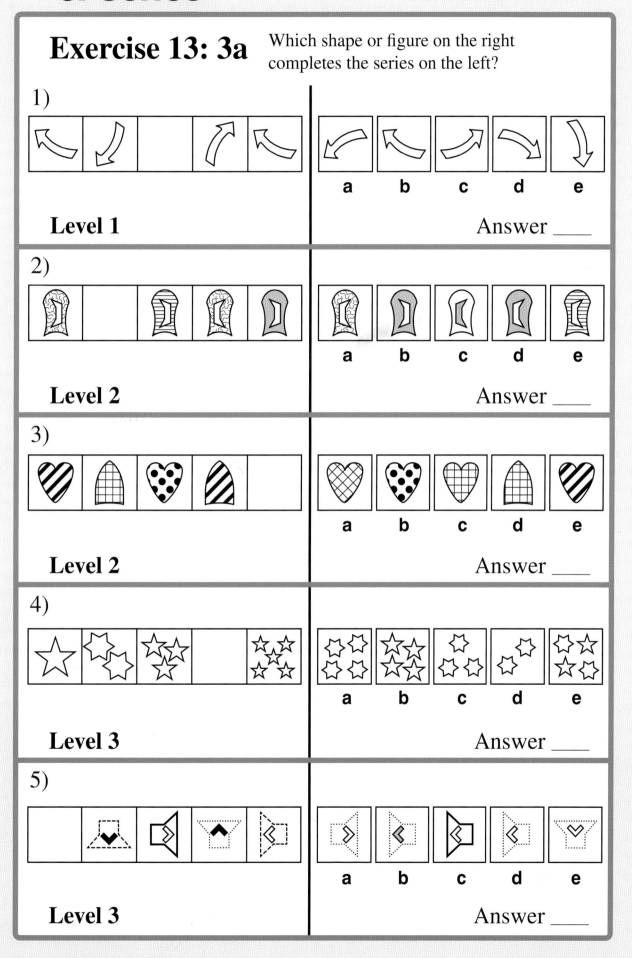

1)

a   b   c   d   e

Level 1

Answer _____

2)

a   b   c   d   e

Level 2

Answer _____

3)

a   b   c   d   e

Level 2

Answer _____

4)

a   b   c   d   e

Level 3

Answer _____

5)

a   b   c   d   e

Level 3

Answer _____

6. Matrices

Exercise 13: 3b

Which shape or figure on the right completes the matrix?

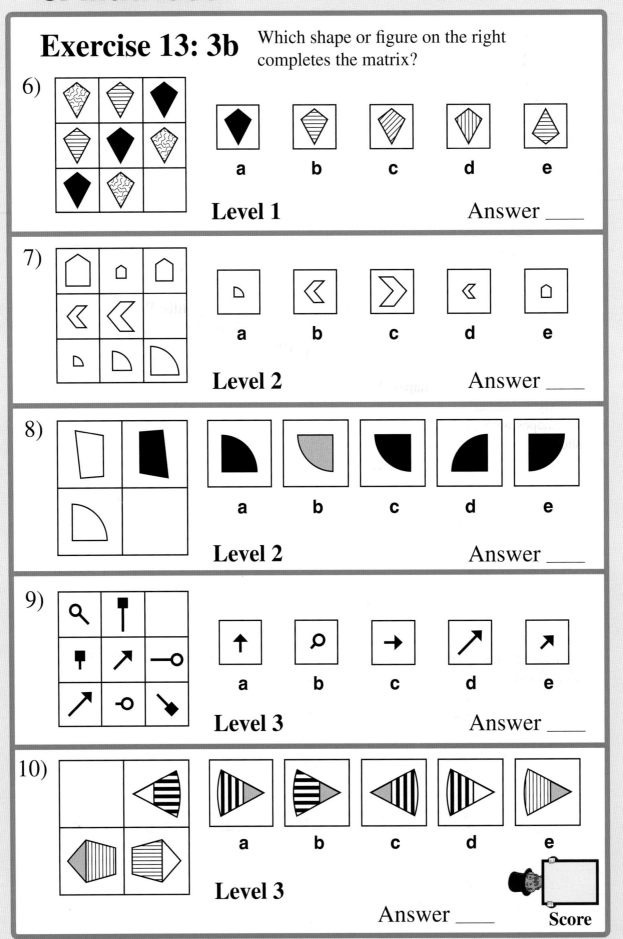

6)

a   b   c   d   e

Level 1

Answer ____

7)

a   b   c   d   e

Level 2

Answer ____

8)

a   b   c   d   e

Level 2

Answer ____

9)

a   b   c   d   e

Level 3

Answer ____

10)

a   b   c   d   e

Level 3

Answer ____   **Score**

Answers

Chapter Seven

Odd One Out

Exercise 7: 1

1) **c** - It is the only shape that does not have a Block Fill.
2) **d** - It has four sides whereas the other shapes all have six sides.
3) **e** - It is a different type of Arrow Shape.
4) **e** - Shapes with a Dashed outline must have an enclosed Black Fill Circle and shapes with a Dotted outline must have an enclosed Grey Fill Circle.
5) **a** - The two enclosed Rectangles have been rotated 90°.
6) **a** - The shaded area does not cover half of the shape.
7) **d** - Curved shapes should have an even number of enclosed Cross Shapes.
8) **b** - The two transposed shapes should be exactly the same.
9) **c** - Shapes with an even number of sides should have an enclosed Square.
10) **a** - The frequency (number) of Circles and Lines should be the same.

Chapter Eight

Codes

Exercise 8: 1

1) **c**
   i) E - Sector Shape; F - Cross Shape.
   ii) S - Grey Fill; T - Black Fill.
2) **d**
   i) P - Cross-hatched Shading Fill; Q - Left Slant Shading Fill.
   ii) J - Large Flower Shape; K - Small Flower Shape.
3) **d**
   i) A - Triangles; B - Squares.
   ii) R - 3 shapes; S - 2 shapes; T - 1 shape.
4) **e**
   i) V, W, X - three Heart Shapes rotated differently.
   ii) G - Speckled Fill; H - Line Fill.
5) **b**
   i) C - House Shape; D - Hexagon.
   ii) O - Solid Line; P - Dashed Line.

6) **b**
   i) Z - Star Shape; Y - Pentagon; X - Chevron Shape.
   ii) M - White Fill; N - Black Fill.
7) **c**
   i) U - Arrow points left; V - Arrow points right.
   ii) F - Dotted Line; G - Solid Line; H- Dashed Line.
8) **a**
   i) J, K, L - fill types.
   ii) R - Large Circle; S - Small Circle; T - Medium Circle.
9) **e**
   i) Cross Shape fills: S - White; T - Black.
   ii) D - Triangle; E - Square; F - Star Shape.
10) **d**
   i) A, B, C - three Keyhole Shapes rotated differently.
   ii) Ellipse fills: L - Black; M - Grey; N - White.

Exercise 8: 2

1) **c**
   i) Fills: C - Black; D - White.
   ii) Rocket Shape direction: X - points left; Y - points up; Z - points right.
2) **c**
   i) Circle fills: S - Black; T - Grey; U - White.
   ii) K, L - Flower Shape orientation.
3) **b**
   i) A - Heart Shape; B - Loaf Shape.
   ii) Line types: D - Solid; E - Dotted; F - Dashed.
4) **e**
   i) P - 2 shapes; Q - 3 shapes; R - 4 shapes.
   ii) Alignment: T - vertical; S - horizontal.
5) **d**
   i) Shape position: X - bottom; Y - top; Z - centre.
   ii) Fills: G - Cross-hatched; H - Line.
6) **a**
   i) Fill type: J - Liquid; K - Line; L - White.
   ii) E, F, G, H - shape size.

Answers

7) **c**
 i) U, V, W, X - shape direction.
 ii) Fill type: L - Black; M - White; N - Grey.
8) **a**
 i) D - Circle; C - Pentagon; B - Square
 ii) Line type: Q - Dotted; R - Dashed;
 S - Solid.
9) **e**
 i) F - Circle; G - Square; H - Hexagon.
 ii) M - Churn Shape; N - Star Shape;
 O - Speaker Shape.
10) **d**
 i) Fill positions: A - Top; B - Bottom.
 ii) Fill types: S - Grey; T - Line; U - Black;
 V - White.

Exercise 8: 3
1) **d**
 i) S - Hexagon horizontal;
 T - Hexagon vertical.
 ii) X - Black Fill; Y - White Fill;
 Z - Grey Fill.
 iii) A, B - direction of Sector Shapes.
2) **d**
 i) F - Grey Fill; G - White Fill.
 ii) A - Arrow points down;
 B - Arrow points up.
 iii) V - Triangle points up;
 W - Triangle points down.
3) **e**
 i) L - Black Fill; M - White Fill.
 ii) R - Star Shape; S - Loaf Shape;
 T - Bone Shape.
 iii) D - Circle; E - Square.
4) **c**
 i) Star fills: P - Grey; Q - Black.
 ii) G - Square; H - No Square.
 iii) C - Small Star Shape;
 B - Large Star Shape.
5) **b**
 i) Fills: J - Cross-hatched; K - White.
 ii) X - Cross Shape; Y - Heart Shape;
 Z - Bean Shape.
 iii) T - Large Circle; U - Small Circle.
6) **c**
 i) A - Grey Fill; B - White Fill.
 ii) S - Triangle; T - Square.
 iii) M - House; N - Oval

7) **a**
 i) X - Small Speaker Shape;
 Y - Large Speaker Shape.
 ii) Shield Shape fills: F - Horizontal Line;
 G - Left Slant; H - Vertical Line.
 iii) Speaker fills: P - White: Q - Black.
8) **b**
 i) R, S, T - direction of Arrow Shape.
 ii) Circle fills: E - Black; F - White.
 iii) L - 2 Circles; M - 1 Circle.
9) **e**
 i) Number of Churn Shapes: P - 2; Q - 3;
 R - 1.
 ii) I - Grey Fill: J - White Fill.
 iii) Z, Y - direction of Churn Shape.
10) **e**
 i) Fill types: O - Black; P - White; Q - Grey.
 ii) E - Circle; F - Ellipse; G - Semi-circle.
 iii) K - Pentagon; L - Hexagon; M - Square.

Chapter Nine
Analogies
Exercise 9: 1
1) **b** - The Linked shapes rotate 180° or
 reflect.
2) **d** - The shapes swap places.
3) **e** - The shape is rotated 90° anticlockwise.
4) **d** - The fills reverse.
5) **a** - Only the linked parts of the shapes
 remain.
6) **c** - The Chevron Shape changes to a Kite
 Shape with the same line type.
7) **c** - The half shape becomes a whole
 shape.
8) **d** - The line types reverse.
9) **b** - The shape reflects on the horizontal
 axis.
10) **a** - Half of the enclosed shapes are
 subtracted.

Exercise 9: 2
1) **e**
 i) The shape is rotated 90° clockwise.
 ii) The line type changes from solid to
 dashed.
2) **e**
 i) The figure is reflected.
 ii) The figure enlarges.

Answers

3) **a**
i) The shape is rotated 90° clockwise.
ii) A reflected shape with a White Fill is added.

4) **e**
i) The fill of the original shape changes to white.
ii) A larger version of the original shape is added at the back.

5) **c**
i) The shape reduces.
ii) The fill rotates 90°.

6) **b**
i) The line type changes from solid to dotted.
ii) A smaller shape is added as an overlay at 90°.

7) **c**
i) The Line rotates 45° anticlockwise.
ii) The line ending fill changes from white to black.

8) **b**
i) The figure rotates 180° or flips vertically.
ii) The shapes swap fills.

9) **d**
i) Another side is added.
ii) The line type changes from Thin Dotted to Thick Solid.

10) **d**
i) The figure rotates 90° clockwise.
ii) The shapes swap places.

Exercise 9: 3

1) **c**
i) The figure rotates 90° clockwise.
ii) The two shapes separate.
iii) The shapes swap fills.

2) **a**
i) The shape enlarges.
ii) The figure rotates 180° or flips vertically.
iii) The shape outline changes from Dotted to Dashed.

3) **a**
i) The shape is flipped horizontally.
ii) A Horizontal Line Fill is added to the shape.
iii) A White Fill Circle is added.

4) **e**
i) An identical shape is overlayed at right angles to the original shape.
ii) The original shape receives a Grey Fill.
iii) The shape created by the intersection has a Left-slant Line Fill.

5) **d**
i) The shape receives a Grey Fill.
ii) The shape is enclosed by a Circle.
iii) Stars are added - the same number as half the number of sides on the shape.

6) **b**
i) The shape is replaced by two shapes.
ii) The number of sides of each of the new shapes is one less than the original shape.
iii) The fill is rotated 90°.

7) **b**
i) The figure rotates 90° anticlockwise.
ii) The shapes swap positions.
iii) The outer shape receives a Liquid Fill.

8) **e**
i) Shapes change from Circles to Squares and vice versa.
ii) The order of the line types reverses.
iii) Two perpendicular lines are added through the middle of the figure.

9) **d**
i) The figure reduces.
ii) The figure rotates 90° anticlockwise.
iii) The fills reverse - White changes to Grey and Grey changes to White.

10) **c**
i) The bottom shape rotates 90°.
ii) The top shape receives a dotted fill.
iii) The two shapes join together.

Chapter Ten
Similarities
Exercise 10: 1

1) **c** - The shape must have 7 sides.
2) **e** - The shape has an order of rotation of 1.
3) **b** - The shape has one line of symmetry.
4) **b** - The shape must have a dashed outline.
5) **d** - The line ending must be at the top of the vertical line.
6) **e** - The shape must have horizontal line shading.

Answers

7) **a** - Half of the shape must be shaded.

8) **b** - The figure must have an enclosed Grey Fill Five-pointed Star.

9) **c** - The shape must be a curved shape.

10) **c** - The shape must have an odd number of sides.

Exercise 10: 2

1) **a**
 i) The outer shape must be a Triangle.
 ii) There must be a Heart Shape with a Grey or Black Fill.

2) **e**
 i) The shape must be curved.
 ii) The fill must be Grey.

3) **d**
 i) The shape must have an even number of sides.
 ii) The outline must be Dashed or Dotted.

4) **b**
 i) The outer shape must be a Shield.
 ii) A Bean Shape must be enclosed.

5) **e**
 i) The bottom shape is a 90° anticlockwise rotation of the top shape.
 ii) There must be a Black Fill shape and a White Fill shape.

6) **c**
 i) The figure must be divided by a Dotted Line.
 ii) The enclosed shape must be in the larger portion of the outside shape.

7) **d**
 i) The outer shape must be curved.
 ii) The enclosed shape must be straight.

8) **c**
 i) The shape must be straight.
 ii) The shape must have a Solid Line Fill.

9) **a**
 i) There must be an Arrow pointing to the left.
 ii) There must be a Circle with a Dotted Fill.

10) **c**
 i) There are three of the same shape in differing sizes.
 ii) One shape must overlay and one shape must merge with the largest shape.

Exercise 10: 3

1) **b**
 i) The main shape must be an Equilateral Triangle.
 ii) There must be an enclosed Circle.
 iii) There must be a 6-sided shape outside of the Triangle.

2) **e**
 i) The number of Cross Shapes should equal half the number of sides of the main shape.
 ii) There should be one Cross Shape with a White Fill.
 iii) The main shape must have a Grey Fill.

3) **e**
 i) There must be an odd number of lines.
 ii) There must be one vertical line.
 iii) There must be one Dashed Line and one Dotted Line.

4) **e**
 i) The main shape must have a Dashed Line.
 ii) There should be four linking shapes.
 iii) Two of the linking shapes must be the same size.

5) **b**
 i) The number of shapes should equal the number of sides of the shape.
 ii) One shape must have a Grey Fill.
 iii) One shape must have a Black Fill Circle.

6) **a**
 i) There must be five shapes.
 ii) One shape must have a Dotted Line.
 iii) The Arrow must have a Triangle Ending.

7) **c**
 i) The Bean Shapes have the same rotation.
 ii) There are an odd number of Lines.
 iii) There must be a Circle with a Line Fill.

8) **c**
 i) The two shapes are at right angles to each other.
 ii) One shape has a Black Fill, one shape has a White Fill.
 iii) The White Fill shape has an enclosed Grey Fill Bone Shape.

Answers

9) **b**
  i) There is a Circle at each corner of the shape.
  ii) Two Circles must have the same fill type, the rest must have different fill types.
  iii) The main shape is a Solid Thick Line type.

10) **a**
  i) The figures are horizontally symmetrical.
  ii) The figures have a Dashed outline.
  iii) Two enclosed shapes must have a White Fill.

Chapter Eleven
Series
Exercise 11: 1

1) **d**
  The shape outline pattern is Solid, Dashed, Dotted, etc.; Repetitive.

2) **c**
  A change in frequency occurs: the number of sides decreases by 2 at each stage; Cumulative.

3) **b**
  The figure rotates 90° clockwise at each stage; Repetitive.

4) **e**
  The shape increases in size at each stage; Cumulative.

5) **e**
  A change in frequency occurs: the number of points increases by 2 at each stage; Cumulative.

6) **a**
  The Sector rotates 45° anticlockwise at each stage; Repetitive.

7) **a**
  One more Arrow Shape is added from alternate sides at each stage; Cumulative.

8) **b**
  The fills pattern is Lattice, Mottled, Dotted, etc.; Repetitive.

9) **b**
  The Cross Shape and the Kite Shape alternate at each stage; Repetitive.

10) **d**
  The Circle rotates clockwise around the Triangle; Repetitive.

Exercise 11: 2

1) **c**
  i) The Loaf Shape rotates 180° at each stage.
  ii) The fill pattern is: Horizontal Line, Vertical Line, Dotted, etc.

2) **e**
  i) The Circle moves (transposes) anticlockwise round the corners of the square at each stage.
  ii) The Circle fill pattern is Grey, White, Black, etc.

3) **a**
  i) The Flower Shape rotates 45° at each stage.
  ii) The enclosed shape pattern is Speaker Shape, Chevron Shape, Sector Shape, etc.

4) **b**
  i) The House Shape rotates 180°, or reflects vertically, at each stage.
  ii) The line type pattern is: Dashed, Dotted, Thick Solid, etc.

5) **b**
  i) The Shape pattern is: Hexagon, Circle, Square, etc.
  ii) Another enclosure is added at each stage.

6) **d**
  i) The Bean Shape rotates 90° anticlockwise at each stage.
  ii) The Arrow rotates 90° clockwise at each stage.

7) **b**
  i) A larger shape follows a smaller shape.
  ii) Fill types: small shape - White; large shape - Cross-hatched.

8) **e**
  i) The shape pattern is: Heart Shape, Cross Shape, Bone Shape, etc.
  ii) One more shape is added at each stage.

9) **e**
  i) The two shapes swap places.
  ii) The shapes swap fill types.

10) **c**
  i) The Arrow rotates 45° anticlockwise at each stage.
  ii) Fill type pattern: Dotted, Speckled, Grey, etc.

Answers

Exercise 11: 3

1) **d**
   i) Stars enclose a Black Fill Circle and Hexagons enclose a White Fill Square.
   ii) The outside shape order is Star, Hexagon, Star, etc.
   iii) One more point is added to the Star each time.

2) **e**
   i) The Triangles flip horizontally at each stage.
   ii) Fill pattern: Vertical Solid Line; Dotted; Cross-hatched.
   iii) Semi-circle position: top, middle, bottom, middle, top, etc.

3) **c**
   i) Shape pattern: Circle, Square; Pentagon, etc.
   ii) Outside shape line type: Dashed, Dotted, Dashed, etc.
   iii) Enclosed shape fill: Black, Grey, White, etc.

4) **b**
   i) The Lines rotate 90° at each stage.
   ii) The Lines become thicker at each stage.
   iii) A Line is added at each stage.

5) **c**
   i) The Hexagon rotates 90° at each stage.
   ii) Hexagon fill type: Mottled, Lattice, Dotted, etc.
   iii) The Sector rotates 90° anticlockwise at each stage.

6) **a**
   i) Circles and Ovals alternate.
   ii) Line type pattern: Thick, Thin, Dotted, etc.
   iii) The Dotted Fill becomes more open at each stage.

7) **d**
   i) Shape pattern: Star, House Shape, Heart Shape, etc.
   ii) The line endings alternate between White Circle and Black Circle.
   iii) The line rotates 90° clockwise at each stage.

8) **d**
   i) The Arrows rotate 45° anticlockwise at each stage.
   ii) The Arrows alternate between large and small.
   iii) Arrow ending types: Closed Straight, Open Straight, Closed Curved, etc.

9) **c**
   i) The shapes alternate between Circles and Triangles.
   ii) Position of shapes: left, centre, right, centre, left, etc.
   iii) One shape is subtracted at each stage.

10) **b**
   i) The enclosed shape becomes the outside shape in the next square.
   ii) Enclosed shape fill pattern: Grey, White Black, etc.
   iii) Outside shape line type: Solid, Dashed, Dotted, etc.

Chapter Twelve
Matrices
Exercise 12: 1

1) **b**
Horizontal: The shape rotates 180° or flips vertically.

2) **c**
Vertical: The shapes swap places.

3) **c**
Horizontal: The shapes swap fills.

4) **a**
Horizontal: The shape rotates 90° anticlockwise on each line.

5) **d**
Diagonal: A diagonal line of reflective symmetry can be drawn through the middle of the matrix.

6) **e**
Vertical and horizontal: There is a small, medium and large Star Shape in each line.
Diagonal: The shapes are the same size.

7) **a**
Vertical and horizontal: The matrix reflects horizontally and vertically.

8) **b**
Horizontal: The shape reduces.
9) **e**
Vertical and horizontal: There is one of each type of figure on each line.
10) **a**
Vertical and horizontal: The shape rotates 45° clockwise each time.

Exercise 12: 2

1) **b** - Solve horizontally.
 i) The shape rotates 90° anticlockwise.
 ii) The line type changes from solid to dotted.
2) **a** - Solve vertically.
 i) Another side is added to the shape.
 ii) The line type changes from Dashed to Solid.
3) **c** - This matrix can be solved in either direction.
 i) Each row and column must have two figures with Circles at the base and one figure with Circles at the top.
 ii) Each row and column must have two figures with two lines and one figure with one line.
4) **d** - Solve horizontally.
 i) One shape becomes two smaller shapes.
 ii) The smaller shapes have a Grey Fill.
5) **d** - Solve horizontally.
 i) The shape reflects horizontally.
 ii) The shape receives a Dotted Fill.
6) **c** - This matrix can be solved in either direction.
 i) The figures rotate 90° anticlockwise at each stage.
 ii) There must be a Circle with a Grey Fill, White Fill and a Black Fill in each row and column.
7) **e** - Solve vertically.
 i) The shape rotates 90° clockwise.
 ii) The bottom half of the shape receives a Mottled Liquid Fill.

8) **a** - This matrix can be solved in either direction.
 i) There must be one of each rotation in each column and row.
 ii) There must be a small, medium and large Cone Shape in each column and row.
9) **a** - Solve vertically.
 i) The shape rotates 90° anticlockwise in each column.
 ii) There must be one of each type of fill in each column and row.
10) **d** - Solve horizontally.
 i) The line types reverse in order.
 ii) The figure reduces in size.

Exercise 12: 3

1) **b** - Solve in either direction.
 i) The figure rotates 90° clockwise at each stage.
 ii) Each row has one of each figure.
 iii) Each row has a small, medium and large figure.
2) **b** - Solve horizontally.
 i) The figure reduces in size.
 ii) The figure rotates 90° anticlockwise.
 iii) The fills reverse.
3) **e** - Solve vertically.
 i) There must be two large and one small shape in each column.
 ii) There must be one of each line type in each row and column: Dotted, Solid, Dashed.
 iii) The shape with the Solid Line type must be rotated 90°.
4) **a** - Solve vertically.
 i) The figure flips vertically or rotates 180°.
 ii) A Line is added.
 iii) The line endings change from White Fill to Black Fill.
5) **d** - Solve in either direction.
 i) Each row/column has a Square, a Circle and a Triangle.
 ii) There is one of each type of fill in each row/column.

Answers

iii) Each row/column has a Black, White and Grey Fill shape.

6) **c** - Solve horizontally.

i) The figure flips or reflects horizontally.

ii) The line type of the outside shape changes to Dashed.

iii) One of the enclosed shapes moves to the outside of the figure.

7) **a** - Solve in either direction.

i) The line rotates 45° clockwise each stage.

ii) Line type pattern: Solid, Dotted, Dashed.

iii) Line ending fills pattern: White, Black, White, etc.

8) **e** - Solve in either direction.

i) The Heart Shape rotates 90° clockwise at each stage.

ii) The outer shape alternates between a Circle and a Square.

iii) There are 1, 2 and 3 Black Fill Circles in each row/column.

9) **b** - Solve horizontally.

i) The figure rotates 180° at each stage.

ii) There must be two enclosures in every row (and column).

iii) There must be a Black Fill enclosed shape in each row (and column).

10) **b** - Solve vertically.

i) The two shapes swap positions.

ii) The two shapes swap fills.

iii) The original top shape rotates 180° or flips vertically.

Chapter Thirteen
Revision
Exercise 13: 1a

1) **b**
2) **a**
3) **c**
4) **e**
5) **d**

Exercise 13: 1b

6) **e**
7) **c**
8) **d**
9) **b**
10) **b**

Exercise 13: 2a

1) **a**
2) **b**
3) **d**
4) **e**
5) **d**

Exercise 13: 2b

6) **b**
7) **c**
8) **a**
9) **d**
10) **a**

Exercise 13: 3a

1) **d**
2) **d**
3) **c**
4) **a**
5) **d**

Exercise 13: 3b

6) **b**
7) **d**
8) **c**
9) **e**
10) **a**

PROGRESS CHARTS

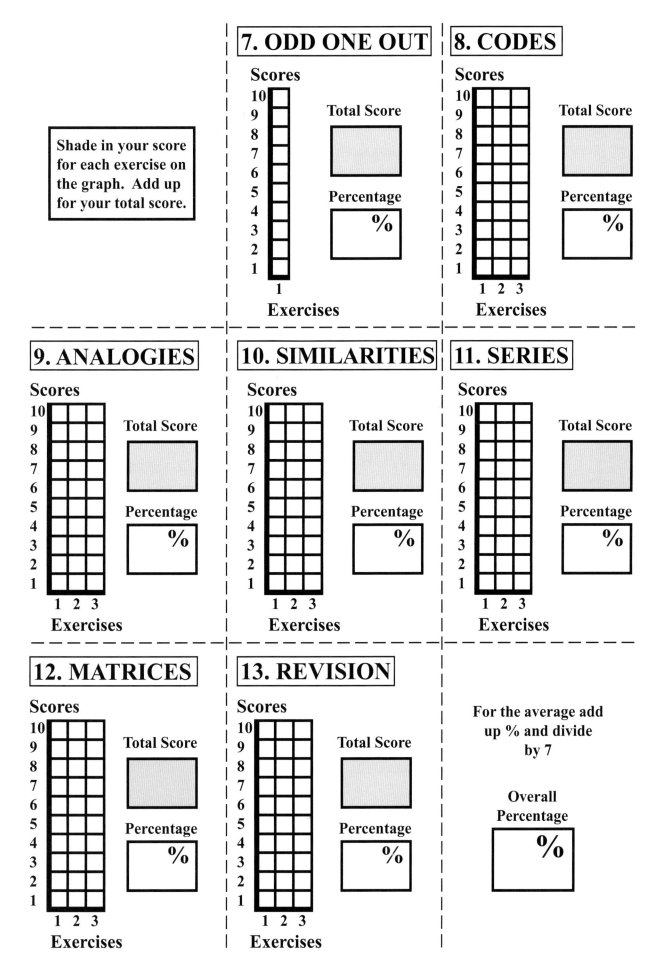

Shade in your score for each exercise on the graph. Add up for your total score.

7. ODD ONE OUT

Scores

Total Score

Percentage %

Exercises

8. CODES

Scores

Total Score

Percentage %

Exercises

9. ANALOGIES

Scores

Total Score

Percentage %

Exercises

10. SIMILARITIES

Scores

Total Score

Percentage %

Exercises

11. SERIES

Scores

Total Score

Percentage %

Exercises

12. MATRICES

Scores

Total Score

Percentage %

Exercises

13. REVISION

Scores

Total Score

Percentage %

Exercises

For the average add up % and divide by 7

Overall Percentage %

CERTIFICATE OF

ACHIEVEMENT

This certifies

_____

has successfully completed

11+ Non-verbal Reasoning
Year 4/5
WORKBOOK **2**

Overall percentage
score achieved   **%**

Comment _____

_____

Signed _____
(teacher/parent/guardian)

Date _____